*INTERNATIONAL SERIES OF MONOGRAPHS IN*
PURE AND APPLIED MATHEMATICS
GENERAL EDITORS:
I. N. SNEDDON, M. STARK AND S. ULAM

VOLUME 86

# SOME TOPICS
# IN COMPLEX ANALYSIS

# Some Topics
# in Complex Analysis

### E. G. PHILLIPS

Sometime Senior Lecturer in Pure Mathematics
University College of North Wales
Bangor

## PERGAMON PRESS

OXFORD · LONDON · EDINBURGH · NEW YORK
PARIS · FRANKFURT

Pergamon Press Ltd., Headington Hill Hall, Oxford
4 & 5 Fitzroy Square, London W.1
Pergamon Press (Scotland) Ltd., 2 & 3 Teviot Place, Edinburgh 1
Pergamon Press Inc., 44–01 21st Street, Long Island City, New York 11101
Pergamon Press S.A.R.L., 24 rue des Écoles, Paris 5ᵉ
Pergamon Press GmbH, Kaiserstrasse 75, Frankfurt-am-Main
Pergamon of Canada Ltd., 6 Adelaide Street East, Toronto, Ontario

First edition 1966

Library of Congress Catalog Card No. 65–28871

SET IN MONOPHOTO TIMES NEW ROMAN AND PRINTED IN
GREAT BRITAIN BY J. W. ARROWSMITH LTD., BRISTOL 3

2433/66

Sep.    Phys.-Math.

# CONTENTS

# PREFACE

THIS book is intended as a sequel to my *Functions of a Complex Variable* in the University Mathematical Texts series. That volume dealt with those parts of the subject normally included in Honours courses; the present book deals with a variety of topics, for the understanding of which a knowledge of the contents of the former book will be assumed.

In a book of this size one could only attempt a brief introduction to the chosen topics and a choice had continually to be made of what to include and what to omit. I have been guided largely by my own interests and predilections, but in making a choice it is often difficult to decide which of two results is the more important from the point of view of inclusion or exclusion.

The first two chapters are based on a course of lectures which I used to give at Bangor. They contain enough to provide a good working knowledge of Elliptic Functions for practical purposes. On the other hand, the Special Functions of Mathematics, Legendre, Bessel and so on, are not included, except to illustrate some contour integrals in the last chapter. Since the subject matter is mainly classical, I am conscious of my indebtedness to most of the existing larger textbooks. Those that I have found most useful I have listed in a bibliography at the end. This list will also suggest sources of further reading on the topics briefly discussed in this book.

The choice of examples has not been easy, especially as some of the topics do not lend themselves to examples other than mere extensions or amplifications of the bookwork, but I hope the collection I have made will be found helpful for fixing the ideas of my readers.

The writing of this book has been made possible because my retirement from my post at Bangor has given me the time to write it. My thanks are due to my former colleague, Mr. S. Moses, who has read the manuscript and made some valuable suggestions. I wish also to thank the publishers for the careful and efficient way in which they have performed their part.

*Bangor*                                                    E. G. PHILLIPS

CHAPTER 1

# ELLIPTIC FUNCTIONS

## 1.1 Definition

Let $\omega_1$, $\omega_2$ be any two complex numbers whose ratio is not wholly real. A function $f(z)$ which satisfies

$$f(z) = f(z + 2\omega_1) = f(z + 2\omega_2),$$

for all values of $z$ for which $f(z)$ exists, is called a *doubly-periodic* (d.p.) function with periods $2\omega_1$, $2\omega_2$. A d.p. function which is meromorphic, i.e. a function which is regular save for poles, is called an *Elliptic Function* (E.F.).

If in the $z$-plane we mark the points $2m\omega_1 + 2n\omega_2$, where $m$, $n$ are integers positive, negative or zero, on joining up these points by straight lines we get a network of parallelograms. These are called *period parallelograms* (p.p.). For all values of $z$ the points $z, z + 2\omega_1, \ldots, z + 2m\omega_1 + 2n\omega_2$ ($m$, $n$ integers) clearly occupy corresponding positions in the various meshes; any pair $z, z'$ of such points are said to be *congruent* and the congruence may be written $z' \equiv z \pmod{2\omega_1, 2\omega_2}$. The value of an E.F. is the same at every one of a set of congruent points; hence its values in any mesh are a repetition of its values in any other mesh.

If $f(z)$ is an E.F. and $c$ a constant, it can be shown that the number of roots of $f(z) = c$ which lie in any p.p. depends on $f(z)$ and not on $c$. This number is the *order* of the E.F. As we shall see, it is the same as the number of poles of $f(z)$ in a p.p. The Weierstrassian E.F. $\wp(u)$ and the Jacobian E.F. sn $u$, cn $u$, dn $u$ are all E.F. of order 2. There are two theorems that we shall assume without proof.† The first is that if $f(z)$ is regular, and not a constant, and if $f(z)$ has a set of periods $2\omega$, $2p\omega$, where $p$ is real, then each of these periods is a multiple of a single fundamental period. The second is that if $f(z)$ is regular and not a constant, and if $f(z)$ has

† See Copson, *Functions of a Complex Variable*, §§ 13.1 to 13.13.

1

periods whose ratio is not real, then $f(z)$ is necessarily doubly-periodic.

## 1.2 Fundamental Theorems

We now consider a number of important theorems in complex variable theory which have special applications to E.F.

THEOREM A. *If the meromorphic function $f(z)$, regular on a closed contour $C$, has $Z$ zeros and $P$ poles inside $C$ (multiple zeros and poles being counted multiply), then*

$$\frac{1}{2\pi i}\int_C \frac{f'(z)}{f(z)}\,dz = Z - P.$$

This theorem is proved in *P.C.V.*, § 40, p. 107.†

THEOREM B. *If $F(z)$ is regular within and on $C$,*

$$\frac{1}{2\pi i}\int_C F(z)\frac{f'(z)}{f(z)}\,dz = \Sigma \text{ values of } F(z) \text{ at the zeros of } f(z)$$

$$- \Sigma \text{ values of } F(z) \text{ at the poles of } f(z).$$

Since $F(z)$ is regular, we have

$$F(z) = F(a)+(z-a)F'(a)+\frac{1}{2!}(z-a)^2 F''(a)+\cdots$$

by Taylor's theorem. Now suppose that $f(z)$ has a zero of order $r$ at $z = a$, then $f(z) = (z-a)^r \phi(z)$, where $\phi(a) \neq 0$. Hence

$$\frac{f'(z)}{f(z)} = \frac{r}{z-a}+\frac{\phi'(z)}{\phi(z)},$$

the last term being regular at $z = a$.

Hence

$$F(z)\frac{f'(z)}{f(z)} = \{F(a)+O(z-a)\}\left\{\frac{r}{z-a}+\text{regular terms}\right\}$$

$$= \frac{rF(a)}{z-a}+\text{regular terms.} \tag{1}$$

† *P.C.V.* denotes my *Functions of a Complex Variable* in the University Mathematical Texts.

Similarly, if $f(z)$ has a pole of order $s$ at $z = a$

$$F(z)\frac{f'(z)}{f(z)} = -\frac{sF(a)}{z-a} + \text{regular terms.} \qquad (2)$$

By applying Cauchy's residue theorem to (1) and (2) the above result follows.

THEOREM C.

$$\frac{1}{2\pi i}\int_C z\frac{f'(z)}{f(z)}\,dz = \Sigma \text{ affixes of zeros} - \Sigma \text{ affixes of poles.}$$

*The affix of a zero or pole is the value of $z$ at that zero or pole.*

This is the special case of Theorem B when $F(z) = z$, but it is stated as a separate theorem because of its important applications.

THEOREM I. *The integral of an E.F. round a p.p. is zero.*

Let $f(z)$ be an E.F. and let $\Pi$ denote a p.p.

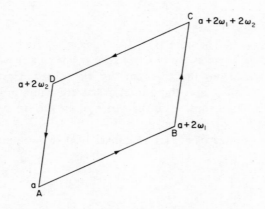

FIG. 1.

$$\int_\Pi f(z)\,dz = \int_a^{a+2\omega_1} \{f(z)-f(z+2\omega_2)\}\,dz$$

$$+ \int_a^{a+2\omega_2} \{f(z+2\omega_1)-f(z)\}\,dz$$

$$= 0 \quad \text{by periodicity.}$$

THEOREM II. *The sum of the residues of an E.F. within a p.p. is zero.*

This follows at once from Theorem I, for

$$\Sigma \text{ Res. at poles of } f(z) \text{ inside } \Pi = \frac{1}{2\pi i} \int_\Pi f(z)\,dz = 0.$$

COROLLARY (to Theorem II). *An E.F. has at least two poles within a p.p.*

An E.F. cannot have no poles, for if it did it would be a mere constant, by Liouville's theorem. It cannot have a simple pole in virtue of the theorem, so it has at least two poles. Hence an E.F. must be at least of order 2.

THEOREM III. *An E.F. has the same number of zeros as poles within a p.p.*

If $f(z) = f(z+2\omega)$, then $f'(z) = f'(z+2\omega)$; thus $f'(z)$ evidently has the same periods as $f(z)$, and so

$$\int_\Pi \frac{f'(z)}{f(z)}\,dz = 0.$$

Hence $Z - P = 0$.

COROLLARY (to Theorem III). *The number of roots of $f(z) = c$ within $\Pi$ is the same as the order of $f(z)$; it does not depend on $c$.*

This follows from the theorem, for the roots of $f(z) = c$ are the zeros of $f(z) - c$ and this function has the same poles as $f(z)$. This justifies the definition of the order of an E.F. in §1.1.

THEOREM IV. *In a p.p.,*

$\Sigma$ affixes of zeros of $f(z) - \Sigma$ affixes of poles $=$ a period.

Referring to Fig. 1,

$$\int_\Pi z\frac{f'(z)}{f(z)}\,dz = \int_{AB} - \int_{DC} + \int_{BC} - \int_{AD}$$

$$= \int_{AB} \left\{ z\frac{f'(z)}{f(z)} - (z+2\omega_1)\frac{f'(z)}{f(z)} \right\} dz$$

$$+ \int_{BC} \left\{ (z+2\omega_2)\frac{f'(z)}{f(z)} - z\frac{f'(z)}{f(z)} \right\} dz$$

$$= 2\omega_2 \int_{BC} \frac{f'(z)}{f(z)}\,dz - 2\omega_1 \int_{AB} \frac{f'(z)}{f(z)}\,dz.$$

Hence

$$\int_\Pi z\frac{f'(z)}{f(z)}\,dz = 2\omega_2[\log f(z)]_B^C - 2\omega_1[\log f(z)]_A^B$$

$$= (2\omega_2 - 2\omega_1)\{\text{multiple of } 2\pi i\}.$$

Hence by Theorem C,

$$\Sigma \text{ affixes of zeros} - \Sigma \text{ affixes of poles} = \frac{1}{2\pi i}\int_\Pi z\frac{f'(z)}{f(z)}\,dz = \text{a period.}$$

### 1.3. The Functions $\wp(u)$, $\sigma(u)$ and $\zeta(u)$

The definitions of these functions, of which the first is the Weierstrassian E.F., depend upon the fact that the double series

$$\sum\sum{}' \frac{1}{(2m\omega_1 + 2n\omega_2)^3},$$

where $m$, $n$ take all integral values (the dash indicating that $m = n = 0$ is excluded) is absolutely convergent. From the theory of double series† an absolutely convergent double series may be deranged, summed in any way we please and transformed into a simple series in any way we please. We are assuming, as always, that the ratio $\omega_2 : \omega_1$ is not real so that the summation extends over all the vertices of parallelograms forming the network, except the origin.

Write $w = 2m\omega_1 + 2n\omega_2$. If $\sum\sum'\{1/|w|^3\}$ converges in any one way then it converges in all possible ways and the series $\sum\sum'\{1/w^3\}$ is absolutely convergent. We show that $\sum\sum'\{1/|w|^3\}$ converges when arranged as a simple series

$$S_1 + S_2 + \ldots + S_r + \ldots, \tag{1}$$

where $S_r$ is the sum of the terms corresponding to points on the perimeter of the $r$th parallelogram concentric with the origin. There are $8r$ points on the $r$th parallelogram and $|w|$ is the distance from the origin to the point at one corner. If $p$ is the length of the shorter of the two perpendiculars from the origin on to a side of the first parallelogram, then for points on the $r$th parallelogram

† See Hyslop, *Infinite Series*, Ch. IX, *et al.*

$|w| \geqslant rp$. Hence,

$$S_r \leqslant \frac{8r}{r^3 p^3} = \frac{8}{p^3} \cdot \frac{1}{r^2}.$$

So the series (1) converges by comparison with $\Sigma(1/r^2)$.

From the absolute convergence of $\Sigma\Sigma'(1/w^3)$ we deduce the absolute convergence of the product

$$\prod_{m=-\infty}^{\infty} \prod_{n=-\infty}^{\infty}{}' \left\{ \left(1 - \frac{u}{w}\right) \exp\left(\frac{u}{w} + \frac{1}{2}\frac{u^2}{w^2}\right) \right\},$$

and the two series

$$\sum_{m=-\infty}^{\infty} \sum_{n=-\infty}^{\infty}{}' \left( \frac{1}{u-w} + \frac{1}{w} + \frac{u}{w^2} \right),$$

$$\sum_{m=-\infty}^{\infty} \sum_{n=-\infty}^{\infty}{}' \left\{ \frac{1}{(u-w)^2} - \frac{1}{w^2} \right\}.$$

For instance, taking the second,

$$\frac{1}{u-w} + \frac{1}{w} + \frac{u}{w^2} \sim \frac{u^2}{w^3}$$

and similarly, by taking logarithms, for the product.†

We now define three functions as follows:

$$\sigma(u) = u \prod\prod{}' \left\{ \left(1 - \frac{u}{w}\right) \exp\left(\frac{u}{w} + \frac{1}{2}\frac{u^2}{w^2}\right) \right\},$$

$$\zeta(u) = \frac{1}{u} + \Sigma\Sigma' \left\{ \frac{1}{u-w} + \frac{1}{w} + \frac{u}{w^2} \right\},$$

$$\wp(u) = \frac{1}{u^2} + \Sigma\Sigma' \left\{ \frac{1}{(u-w)^2} - \frac{1}{w^2} \right\}. \tag{2}$$

Of these three functions, only the last is an E.F. Evidently, from the above,

$$\zeta(u) = \frac{d}{du} \log \sigma(u) = \frac{\sigma'(u)}{\sigma(u)} \quad \text{and} \quad \wp(u) = -\frac{d}{du}\zeta(u).$$

Since, in (2), values of $w$ occur in pairs, odd powers of $u$ vanish, so $\wp(u)$ is an even function. Once the Weierstrassian E.F. $\wp(u)$ has been defined, we do not make much use of the definition.

† The symbol $\sim$ is used for "behaves like".

Most of its properties can be proved by use of the theorems in § 1.2 and the theorems which constitute the method of comparison now to be proved.

## 1.4 The Method of Comparison

The method depends upon two simple but powerful theorems depending on Liouville's theorem. Let $f(u)$ and $\phi(u)$ denote two E.F., then

(I) *If $f(u)$ and $\phi(u)$ have the same periods, the same zeros and the same poles then $f(u) = C\phi(u)$, where $C$ is a constant.*

(II) *If $f(u)$ and $\phi(u)$ have the same periods, the same poles and the same principal parts at those poles then $f(u) - \phi(u) = C$.*

To prove (I), consider $g(u) = f(u)/\phi(u)$. Then $g(u)$ is doubly-periodic and has no singularities, for $g(u)$ can only be singular where (a) $f(u)$ has a pole, or (b) $\phi(u)$ has a zero. Since the poles of $\phi(u)$ neutralize those of $f(u)$ and the zeros of $f(u)$ those of $\phi(u)$, $g(u)$ has no singularities and so, by Liouville's theorem, $g(u) = C$.

To prove (II) similarly, we observe that $h(u) = f(u) - \phi(u)$ has no singularities. The method of comparison is used frequently in the theory of the E.F. $\wp(u)$. We shall see later that it is of use also for Jacobian E.F. sn $u$, cn $u$, dn $u$.

## 1.5 The Double Periodicity of $\wp(u)$

We deduce this by considering the derivative $\wp'(u)$.

$$\wp'(u) = -\frac{2}{u^3} - \sum\sum' \frac{2}{(u-w)^3} = -2\sum\sum \frac{1}{(u-w)^3}.$$

$\wp'(u)$ is obviously doubly-periodic (d.p.), for the addition of $2\omega_1$, $2\omega_2$ to $u$ merely displaces the origin of the lattice-work, but does not affect the points over which the summation extends. Hence

$$\wp'(u+2\omega) = \wp'(u),$$

where $\omega$ is used for either $\omega_1$ or $\omega_2$.

On integration

$$\wp(u+2\omega) = \wp(u) + C.$$

Put $u = -\omega$; then $\wp(\omega) = \wp(-\omega) + C$ and since $\wp(u)$ is even, it follows that $C = 0$.

## 1.6 Descriptive Properties of $\wp(u)$, $\sigma(u)$ and $\zeta(u)$

$\wp(u)$ is one-valued, meromorphic and even. It is doubly-periodic with principal part like $1/u^2$ at each of the period points.

$\zeta(u)$ is one-valued and meromorphic; it is not d.p. but as we see below, adds on a constant; it has a simple pole with residue 1 at each of the period points.

$\sigma(u)$ is one-valued and integral; it is not d.p. but multiplies by a non-constant factor; it has a simple zero at each of the period points.

We introduce, for convenience of symmetry, a third number $\omega_3$, defined by $\omega_3 = -(\omega_1 + \omega_2)$, where $2\omega_1$, $2\omega_2$ are the periods of $\wp(u)$.

Since $\wp(u + 2\omega) = \wp(u)$ we get on integration, since

$$\frac{d}{du}\zeta(u) = -\wp(u), \qquad \zeta(u + 2\omega) = \zeta(u) + C.$$

Put $u = -\omega$ then $\zeta(\omega) = \zeta(-\omega) + C$; but $\zeta(u)$ is odd, so $C = 2\zeta(\omega)$. We write

$$\eta_r = \zeta(\omega_r) \qquad (r = 1, 2, 3)$$

and so

$$\zeta(u + 2\omega_r) = \zeta(u) + 2\eta_r.$$

If we now integrate again we get

$$\log \sigma(u + 2\omega) = \log \sigma(u) + 2\eta u + \log C$$

or

$$\sigma(u + 2\omega) = C\, e^{2\eta u}\sigma(u)$$

and again, on putting $u = -\omega$, since the $\sigma$-function is odd,

$$\sigma(u + 2\omega) = -e^{2\eta(u + \omega)}\sigma(u).$$

## 1.7 The Addition Theorem for $\wp(u)$

*If* $x + y + z = $ period,

$$\begin{vmatrix} \wp(x) & \wp(y) & \wp(z) \\ \wp'(x) & \wp'(y) & \wp'(z) \\ 1 & 1 & 1 \end{vmatrix} = 0.$$

Assume that $z$ is a complex variable and $x$, $y$ two complex numbers in the same p.p. as $z$. Let $f(z)$ denote the above determinant, then $f(z)$ is an E.F. of order 3 with a triple pole at $z = 0$, in virtue of the term $\wp'(z)$. Hence by Theorem III, §1.2, it has three zeros. Two of these are obviously $z = x$, $z = y$. Let the third unknown simple zero be $\zeta$ then, using Theorem IV, $x+y+\zeta-0 =$ period, hence

$$\zeta = -(x+y) + \text{a period.}$$

If $x$, $y$ are not in the same p.p. as $z$, we replace them by congruent points which are. This proves the result.

Since $z = \text{period} - (x+y)$, $\wp(z) = \wp(-x-y) = \wp(x+y)$ since $\wp(z)$ is even. $\wp'(z) = \wp'(-x-y) = -\wp'(x+y)$ since $\wp'(z)$ is odd, so the addition theorem may be written

$$\begin{vmatrix} \wp(x) & \wp(y) & \wp(x+y) \\ \wp'(x) & \wp'(y) & -\wp'(x+y) \\ 1 & 1 & 1 \end{vmatrix} = 0. \tag{1}$$

Since, as we shall see in §1.8, the derivatives occurring in (1) can be expressed algebraically in terms of $\wp(x)$, $\wp(y)$, $\wp(x+y)$, (1) really expresses $\wp(x+y)$ algebraically in terms of $\wp(x)$ and $\wp(y)$. (1) is therefore an addition theorem for the $\wp$-function. Other forms of the addition theorem follow later.

## 1.8 The Relation Between $\wp(u)$ and $\wp'(u)$

In the neighbourhood of the origin, as we have seen in the definition of $\wp(u)$ in §1.3,

$$\wp(u) = \frac{1}{u^2} + c_1 u^2 + c_2 u^4 + \ldots$$

$$\wp'(u) = -\frac{2}{u^3} + 2c_1 u + 4c_2 u^3 + \ldots$$

so

$$\wp'^2(u) = \frac{4}{u^6} - \frac{8c_1}{u^2} - 16c_2 - \ldots$$

which clearly has the same principal part as $4\wp^3(u) - \lambda\wp(u)$ if $\lambda$ is suitably chosen.

2

$$4\wp^3(u) - \lambda\wp(u) = 4\left\{\frac{1}{u^2} + c_1 u^2 + \ldots\right\}^3 - \lambda\left(\frac{1}{u^2} + c_1 u^2 + \ldots\right)$$

$$= \frac{4}{u^6} + \frac{12c_1}{u^2} - \frac{\lambda}{u^2} + O(u^2).$$

Hence

$$-8c_1 = 12c_1 - \lambda \quad \text{so} \quad \lambda = 20c_1.$$

Hence by method of comparison (II), $\wp'^2(u)$ and $4\wp^3(u) - 20c_1\wp(u)$ differ by a constant $\mu$, say.

So

$$\wp'^2(u) = 4\wp^3(u) - 20c_1\wp(u) + \mu,$$

and comparing constant terms

$$\mu = -28c_2,$$

so

$$\wp'^2(u) = 4\wp^3(u) - 20c_1\wp(u) - 28c_2.$$

This is usually written,

$$\wp'^2(u) = 4\wp^3(u) - g_2\wp(u) - g_3, \tag{1}$$

where $g_2 = 20c_1$, $g_3 = 28c_2$; $g_2$ and $g_3$ are called the *invariants* of $\wp(u)$.

By going back to the double series definition of $\wp(u)$, since $w \equiv 2m\omega_1 + 2n\omega_2$ we have

$$\frac{1}{(u-w)^2} - \frac{1}{w^2} = \frac{1}{w^2}\left\{\left(1 - \frac{u}{w}\right)^{-2} - 1\right\} = \frac{1}{w^2}\left\{\frac{2u}{w} + \frac{3u^2}{w^2} + \ldots\right\},$$

if

$$|u| < |w|.$$

Thus,

$$\wp(u) - \frac{1}{u^2} = 2\sum\sum'\frac{1}{w^3}\cdot u + 3\sum\sum'\frac{1}{w^4}\cdot u^2 + \ldots$$

On writing

$$\sum\sum'\frac{1}{w^k} = S_k \ (k > 2)$$

we have

$$\wp(u) - \frac{1}{u^2} = 2S_3 u + 3S_4 u^2 + 4S_5 u^3 + 5S_6 u^4 + \ldots$$

but, since the values of $w$ concerned occur in pairs, the coefficients of the odd powers of $u$ vanish, so

$$\wp(u) = \frac{1}{u^2} + 3s_4 u^2 + 5s_6 u^4 + \ldots$$

On comparing with the series as previously written,

$$\wp(u) = \frac{1}{u^2} + c_1 u^2 + c_2 u^4 + \ldots$$

we find that $c_1 = 3s_4$, $c_2 = 5s_6$, $c_3 = 7s_8, \ldots$; hence the so-called invariants $g_2$, $g_3$ are given by

$$g_2 = 20c_1 = 60s_4, \qquad g_3 = 28c_2 = 140s_6.$$

From $\wp(u+2\omega) = \wp(u)$ we get $\wp'(u+2\omega) = \wp'(u)$ and on putting $u = -\omega$, $\wp'(\omega) = \wp'(-\omega)$. But since $\wp'(u)$ is odd it follows that $\wp'(\omega) = 0$. If we write $\wp'(\omega_r) = e_r$, $(r = 1, 2, 3)$, then, since $\wp'(u)$ vanishes for $u = \omega_1, \omega_2, \omega_3$

$$4\wp^3(u) - g_2\wp(u) - g_3 = 4(\wp(u) - e_1)(\wp(u) - e_2)(\wp(u) - e_3)$$

and it follows that

$$e_1 + e_2 + e_3 = 0$$

$$e_1 e_2 + e_1 e_3 + e_2 e_3 = -\tfrac{1}{4}g_2$$

$$e_1 e_2 e_3 = \tfrac{1}{4}g_3.$$

If we put $z = \wp(u)$, then, on using eqn. (1),

$$\frac{\mathrm{d}z}{\mathrm{d}u} = \sqrt{(4z^3 - g_2 z - g_3)}.$$

Now when $u = 0$, $z = \infty$ and so

$$u = \int_{\infty}^{z} \frac{\mathrm{d}t}{\sqrt{(4t^3 - g_2 t - g_3)}}.$$

The two branches of the integrand give equal and opposite values of $u$, which correspond to the same value of $z$, since $\wp(u)$ is even.

## 1.9 Another Form of the Addition Theorem

Starting with the result, proved in §1.7, we have

$$\begin{vmatrix} \wp(u) & \wp(v) & \wp(w) \\ \wp'(u) & \wp'(v) & \wp'(w) \\ 1 & 1 & 1 \end{vmatrix} = 0$$

if $w \equiv u$, $w \equiv v$, $w \equiv -(u+v)$.

On expanding and rearranging the determinant,

$$\wp'(w)\{\wp(u) - \wp(v)\} = \wp(w)\{\wp'(u) - \wp'(v)\} + \wp(u)\wp'(v) - \wp'(u)\wp(v).$$

Square this and substitute for $\wp'^2(w)$; we get a cubic in $z = \wp(w)$,

$$4\{\wp(u) - \wp(v)\}^2 z^3 - \{\wp'(u) - \wp'(v)\}^2 z^2 + \ldots = 0.$$

The sum of the roots of this cubic is plainly

$$\frac{1}{4}\left\{\frac{\wp'(u) - \wp'(v)}{\wp(u) - \wp(v)}\right\}^2;$$

but we know that the roots are $z = \wp(u)$, $\wp(v)$, $\wp(u+v)$ so

$$\wp(u+v) + \wp(u) + \wp(v) = \frac{1}{4}\left\{\frac{\wp'(u) - \wp'(v)}{\wp(u) - \wp(v)}\right\}^2. \tag{1}$$

## 1.10 Fundamental Expressions of E.F.

We now show that any E.F. can be expressed in any of the following three ways. Many fundamental formulae can be deduced in this way.

A. In terms of the $\sigma$-function.

B. In terms of the $\zeta$-function and its derivatives.

C. In terms of $\wp(u)$ and $\wp'(u)$.

Let $f(u)$ be the E.F. considered in each case.

CASE A. Suppose that $f(u)$ has $a_1, a_2, \ldots, a_n$ as a set of distinct zeros and $b_1, b_2, \ldots, b_n$ a set of distinct poles. By Theorem III, § 1.2, there will be the same number of each in a p.p. On using Theorem IV, $\Sigma a - \Sigma b = $ period, and we can arrange by the addition or subtraction of periods that $\Sigma a = \Sigma b$.

Now consider

$$\phi(u) = \frac{\sigma(u - a_1)\sigma(u - a_2) \ldots \sigma(u - a_n)}{\sigma(u - b_1)\sigma(u - b_2) \ldots \sigma(u - b_n)}.$$

On increasing $u$ by $2\omega$ we find that $\phi(u)$ is multiplied by the factor

$$\frac{(-1)^n \exp\{2\eta(u-a_1+\omega+u-a_2+\omega+\ldots+u-a_n+\omega)\}}{(-1)^n \exp\{2\eta(u-b_1+\omega+u-b_2+\omega+\ldots+u-b_n+\omega)\}}.$$

Since $\Sigma a = \Sigma b$ this multiplying factor is 1. Hence $\phi(u)$ has the same periods as $f(u)$. Clearly $\phi(u)$ and $f(u)$ have the same zeros and poles, so by the method of comparison $f(u) = C\phi(u)$.

CASE B. Suppose, to fix the ideas, that $f(u)$ has three poles $a$, $b$, $c$ in a p.p. and let the principal parts at these poles be,

$$\frac{A_1}{u-a}+\frac{A_2}{(u-a)^2}+\ldots+\frac{A_r}{(u-a)^r},$$

$$\frac{B_1}{u-b}+\frac{B_2}{(u-b)^2}+\ldots+\frac{B_s}{(u-b)^s},$$

$$\frac{C_1}{u-c}+\frac{C_2}{(u-c)^2}+\ldots+\frac{C_t}{(u-c)^t}.$$

Consider

$$\phi(u) = A_1\zeta(u-a)-A_2\zeta'(u-a)+\ldots+\frac{(-1)^{r-1}A_r\zeta^{(r-1)}(u-a)}{(r-1)!}$$

$$+B_1\zeta(u-b)-\ldots$$

$$+C_1\zeta(u-c)-\ldots$$

Since $\phi(u)$ plainly has the same poles and principal parts at the poles as $f(u)$, then $f(u)-\phi(u) = C$, provided that $\phi(u)$ has the same periods as $f(u)$. The only possible non-periodic terms in $\phi(u)$ are

$$A_1\zeta(u-a)+B_1\zeta(u-b)+C_1\zeta(u-c).$$

On increasing $u$ by $2\omega$ the last expression increases by

$$2\eta(A_1+B_1+C_1).$$

But since $A_1+B_1+C_1$ is the sum of the residues of $f(u)$ this must be zero, in virtue of Theorem II, § 1.2.

CASE C. (1) Let $f(u)$ be even and ·suppose the set of zeros $\pm a_1, \pm a_2, \ldots, \pm a_n$ and the set of poles $\pm b_1, \pm b_2, \ldots, \pm b_n$ are such that every zero (pole) is congruent to one of them. Suppose also that $u = 0$ is neither a pole nor a zero. Then clearly

$$f(u) = C\frac{\{\wp(u) - \wp(a_1)\} \dots \{\wp(u) - \wp(a_n)\}}{\{\wp(u) - \wp(b_1)\} \dots \{\wp(u) - \wp(b_n)\}},$$

by the principle of comparison. The right-hand side admits $a_1, a_2, \dots, a_n$ as zeros and, since $\wp(u)$ is even, it also admits $-a_1, -a_2, \dots, -a_n$. Similarly for the poles.

(2) *If $f(u)$ is any E.F.* we can write $f(u) = \phi(u) + \psi(u)$, where $\phi(u)$ is the even function $\frac{1}{2}\{f(u) + f(-u)\}$ and $\psi(u)$ is the odd function $\frac{1}{2}\{f(u) - f(-u)\}$. Then

$$f(u) = \phi(u) + \frac{\psi(u)}{\wp'(u)} \cdot \wp'(u).$$

Plainly $\phi(u)$ and $\psi(u)/\wp'(u)$ are both even and so expressible as above. We note that when $f(u)$ is even it is expressible in terms of $\wp(u)$ alone. There remain the cases in which $u = 0$ is either a pole or zero of $f(u)$.

Suppose $u = 0$ is a pole of order $2q$ of $f(u)$ and let the other poles be $\pm b_1, \pm b_2, \dots, \pm b_{n-q}$. Then

$$f(u) = C\frac{\{\wp(u) - \wp(a_1)\} \dots \{\wp(u) - \wp(a_n)\}}{\{\wp(u) - \wp(b_1)\} \dots \{\wp(u) - \wp(b_{n-q})\}},$$

for the right-hand side has simple poles at $\pm b_1, \pm b_2, \dots \pm b_{n-q}$ and also a pole of order $2q$ at $u = 0$. Since $u = 0$ is a pole of order $2n$ of the numerator and of order $2(n-q)$ of the denominator, it is a pole of order $2q$ of the whole. Similarly if $u = 0$ is a zero of order $2s$ of $f(u)$ and the others are $\pm a_1, \pm a_2, \dots, \pm a_{n-s}$ then

$$f(u) = C\frac{\{\wp(u) - \wp(a_1)\} \dots \{\wp(u) - \wp(a_{n-s})\}}{\{\wp(u) - \wp(b_1)\} \dots \{\wp(u) - \wp(b_n)\}}.$$

### 1.11 Some Fundamental Formulae

(I) Let $f(u) = \wp(u) - \wp(v)$. Since $f(u)$ is of order 2, with zeros $\pm v$† and poles 0, 0, then by Case A,

$$f(u) = C\frac{\sigma(u+v)\sigma(u-v)}{\sigma^2(u)}.$$

† If $v$ and $-v$ are not in a p.p. we can replace them by conjugate points which are.

Multiply by $u^2$ and then make $u \to 0$. Since

$$u^2 \wp(u) \to 1 \qquad \text{and} \qquad \frac{u^2}{\sigma^2(u)} \to 1$$

we get

$$1 = C\sigma(v)\sigma(-v) = -C\sigma^2(v).$$

Hence,

$$\wp(u) - \wp(v) = -\frac{\sigma(u+v)\sigma(u-v)}{\sigma^2(u)\sigma^2(v)} \tag{W}$$

(W) is Weierstrass's fundamental formula from which a number of others can be deduced. We give a few examples here.

(II) *The addition formula for* $\zeta(u)$. Differentiate (W) logarithmically with respect to $u$; then with respect to $v$, we obtain

$$\frac{\wp'(u)}{\wp(u) - \wp(v)} = \zeta(u+v) + \zeta(u-v) - 2\zeta(u),$$

$$\frac{-\wp'(v)}{\wp(u) - \wp(v)} = \zeta(u+v) - \zeta(u-v) - 2\zeta(v),$$

which give, on addition,

$$\zeta(u+v) - \zeta(u) - \zeta(v) = \frac{1}{2}\frac{\wp'(u) - \wp'(v)}{\wp(u) - \wp(v)} \cdots \tag{X}$$

(III) *A third form of the addition theorem for* $\wp(u)$. On writing $P(u, v)$ for twice the right-hand side of (X) and differentiating with respect to $u$,

$$\wp(u) - \wp(u+v) = \frac{1}{2}\frac{\partial}{\partial u}P(u, v) \tag{Y}$$

(IV) *Duplication formula for* $\wp(u)$. Make $u \to v$ in (X), then

$$\zeta(2v) - 2\zeta(v) = \frac{1}{2}\lim_{u \to v} P(u, v) = \frac{1}{2}\lim_{u \to v}\frac{\wp''(u)}{\wp'(u)} = \frac{1}{2}\frac{\wp''(v)}{\wp'(v)}, \tag{1}$$

so long as $\wp'(v) \neq 0$.

From (1), on differentiation, we get

$$-2\wp(2v) + 2\wp(v) = \frac{1}{2}\frac{\wp'(v)\wp'''(v) - \wp''^2(v)}{\wp'^2(v)}. \tag{2}$$

Now

$$\wp'^2(v) = 4\,\wp^3(v) - g_2\,\wp(v) - g_3,$$

$$\wp''(v) = 6\,\wp^2(v) - \tfrac{1}{2}g_2,$$

$$\wp'''(v) = 12\,\wp(v)\,\wp'(v),$$

and substituting in the right-hand side of (2) we get

$$\wp(2v) + 2\,\wp(v) = \frac{1}{4}\left\{\frac{\wp''(v)}{\wp'(v)}\right\}^2. \tag{Z}$$

This result can also be deduced by putting $u = v$, and taking the limit as $u \to v$ on the right-hand side of formula (1) in § 1.9.

### 1.12 Example

To illustrate Case C we solve the example:

*Express $\wp(z-\alpha) - \wp(z+\alpha)$ in terms of $\wp(z)$ and $\wp'(z)$.* Since $f(z) = \wp(z-\alpha) - \wp(z+\alpha)$ is odd, $\phi(z) = [\wp(z-\alpha) - \wp(z+\alpha)]/\wp'(z)$ is even and so, by Case C, we can express $\phi(z)$ in terms of $\wp(z)$ only.

On expanding $\wp(z-\alpha)$ and $\wp(z+\alpha)$ in powers of $z$ by Taylor's theorem and using the fact that

$$\wp'(z) = -\frac{2}{z^3} + O(z),$$

we easily find that near $z = 0$,

$$\phi(z) = z^4\,\wp'(\alpha) + \dots$$

so that $\phi(z)$ has a zero of order 4 at $z = 0$. Choose a p.p. which contains the point $z = 0$.

We easily show that $\phi(z)$ has a pole of order 2 at $z = \alpha$ and at $z = -\alpha$, or at congruent points to these in the p.p.

It follows from Case C (the case in which $u = 0$ is a zero) and the method of comparison, § 1.4, that

$$\phi(z) = C\{\wp(z) - \wp(\alpha)\}^{-2}.$$

If $z$ is small,

$$z^4\,\wp'(\alpha) + \dots = \frac{C}{\{z^{-2} + O(z^2) - \wp(\alpha)\}^2} = \frac{Cz^4}{1 + O(z^2)}$$

so $C = \wp'(\alpha)$. Hence

$$\wp(z-\alpha) - \wp(z+\alpha) = \wp'(\alpha)\wp'(z)\{\wp(z) - \wp(\alpha)\}^{-2}.$$

This example, chosen to illustrate Case C, can be more easily proved by using formula (1) of § 1.9. This is suggested as an exercise for the reader.

## Examples 1

**1.** If $S_k$ denotes the sum of the series $\Sigma\Sigma'(2m\omega_1 + 2n\omega_2)^{-k}$, where $k > 2$, prove that (i) $7S_8 = 3S_4^2$, (ii) $5S_4S_6 = 11S_{10}$.

**2.** Prove that

$$\wp(u) + \wp(u+\omega_1) + \wp(u+\omega_2) + \wp(u+\omega_1+\omega_2) = 4\wp(2u)$$

(i) by considering the roots of the equation $\wp(2z) = \wp(2u)$, (ii) by the method of comparison.

**3.** Prove that

$$\begin{vmatrix} 1 & \wp(u) & \wp'(u) \\ 1 & \wp(v) & \wp'(v) \\ 1 & \wp(w) & \wp'(w) \end{vmatrix} = \frac{2\sigma(u-v)\sigma(v-w)\sigma(w-u)\sigma(u+v+w)}{\sigma^3(u)\sigma^3(v)\sigma^3(w)}.$$

**4.** Show that

$$\wp(z+y) + \wp(z-y) = \frac{\{\wp(z) + \wp(y)\}\{2\wp(z)\wp(y) - \tfrac{1}{2}g_2\} - g_3}{\{\wp(z) - \wp(y)\}^2}.$$

**5.** Prove that

(i) $\dfrac{d}{du}\{\wp(u+\omega_1) - e_1\}\{\wp(u) - e_1\} = 0$;

(ii) $\wp(u+\omega_1) - e_1 = \dfrac{(e_1 - e_2)(e_1 - e_3)}{\wp(u) - e_1}$

and find similar expressions for $\wp(u+\omega_3) - e_3$, $\wp(u+\omega_1+\omega_2) - e_2$.

**6.** (i) Show that if $u+v+w = 0$

$$\{\zeta(u) + \zeta(v) + \zeta(w)\}^2 = \wp(u) + \wp(v) + \wp(w).$$

(ii) Prove that

$$\frac{\wp'(u) - \wp'(v)}{\wp(u) - \wp(v)} = 2\zeta(u+v) - 2\zeta(u) - 2\zeta(v),$$

by using the method of comparison. (Proved otherwise in § 1.11.)

**7.** Show that

(i) $\wp(u)\wp(v)\wp(u+v) - \wp(\omega_1)\wp(\omega_2)\wp(\omega_1+\omega_2) = \dfrac{1}{4}\left\{\dfrac{\wp(u)\wp'(v) - \wp(v)\wp'(u)}{\wp(u) - \wp(v)}\right\}^2,$

(ii) $27\{\wp'^2(z) + g_3\}^2 = 2\wp''^3(z) - 3g_2\wp''^2(z) + g_2^3.$

**8.** If $F(z) = \wp(z) - \wp(\tfrac{1}{2}\omega_1)$, show that

$$F(z)F(z+\tfrac{1}{2}\omega_1)F(z+\omega_1)F(z+\tfrac{3}{2}\omega_1) = 4F^2(\omega_1)F(\omega_2)F(\omega_3).$$

**9.** (i) If $3u$ is a period of $\wp(u)$ but $u$ is not, show that

$$\wp'(u)\wp'''(u) = \wp''^2(u).$$

(ii) If $3\alpha$ is a period of $\wp(u)$, but $\alpha$ is not, show that

$$\{\wp(u) - \wp(\alpha)\}\{\wp(u+\alpha) - \wp(\alpha)\}\{\wp(u+2\alpha) - \wp(\alpha)\} = -\wp'^2(\alpha).$$

**10.** Prove that

(i) $4\wp(u)\wp(v)\wp(u+v) = g_3 + \left\{\dfrac{\wp(u)\wp'(v) - \wp(v)\wp'(u)}{\wp(u) - \wp(v)}\right\}^2,$

(ii) $\dfrac{\wp'(z+\omega_1)}{\wp'(z)} = \dfrac{(e_1-e_2)(e_3-e_1)}{\{\wp(z)-e_1\}^2}.$

**11.** Prove that

(i) $\sigma(2z) = \dfrac{2\sigma(z)\sigma(z-\omega_1)\sigma(z-\omega_2)\sigma(z+\omega_1+\omega_2)}{\sigma(\omega_1)\sigma(\omega_2)\sigma(\omega_1+\omega_2)},$

(ii) $\dfrac{\sigma(3z)}{\sigma^9(z)} = 3\wp(z)\wp'^2(z) - \tfrac{1}{4}\wp''^2(z).$

**12.** (i) Prove that the sum of

$$\wp\left(\frac{2\omega_1}{3}\right), \qquad \wp\left(\frac{2\omega_3}{3}\right), \qquad \wp\left(\frac{2\omega_1+2\omega_3}{3}\right), \qquad \wp\left(\frac{2\omega_1-2\omega_3}{3}\right)$$

is zero and find their product.

(ii) Prove that

$$\wp^{(\text{VI})}(z) = 7!\left\{\wp^4(z) - \frac{g_2}{5}\wp^2(z) - \frac{g_3}{7}\wp(z)\right\} + 9g_2^2.$$

**13.** If

$$2z = \frac{\wp'(u) - \wp'(a)}{\wp(u) - \wp(a)},$$

prove that

$$\left(\frac{dz}{du}\right)^2 = z^4 - 6z^2 \wp(a) + 4z \wp'(a) + 9 \wp^2(a) - 2 \wp''(a).$$

**14.** Prove that

(i) $2\wp'(z + \omega_1)\{\wp(z) - \wp(\omega_1)\}^2 + \wp'(z)\wp''(\omega_1) = 0$,

(ii) $\dfrac{\wp'(z)}{\{\wp(z) - \wp(u)\}^2} = \dfrac{2\sigma(z)\sigma^4(u)}{\sigma^2(z-u)\sigma^2(z+u)} \displaystyle\prod_{r=1}^{3} \dfrac{\sigma(z-\omega_r)}{\sigma(\omega_r)}.$

**15.** (i) Express $\wp'(u)\wp'(2u)$ as a rational function of $\wp(u)$.

(ii) Show that it is possible to determine constants $\alpha$ and $\beta$ so that

$$\frac{\alpha\sigma^2(z) + \beta\sigma(z+a)\sigma(z-a)}{\sigma(z+b)\sigma(z-b)}$$

is a constant.

**16.** Prove that

(i) $2\zeta(2z) = \zeta(z) + \zeta(z - \omega_1) + \zeta(z + \omega_1 + \omega_2) + \zeta(z - \omega_2)$,

(ii) $\zeta(z + 2x) - \zeta(z) + \zeta(y) - \zeta(2x + y)$

$$= \frac{\wp'(x)\{\wp(z+x) - \wp(x+y)\}}{\{\wp(x+y) - \wp(x)\}\{\wp(z+x) - \wp(x)\}}.$$

## CHAPTER 2

# THE JACOBIAN ELLIPTIC FUNCTIONS

## 2.1 The Periods of an Integral

Consider first

$$I = \int_0^z f(z)\,dz, \qquad \text{where} \qquad f(z) = (1-z^2)^{-\frac{1}{2}}.$$

The integrand has branch points at $z = \pm 1$. Let us choose the value of $f(z)$ so that initially $f(z) = 1$. Consider a contour consisting of two loops $A$ and $B$ round the branch points.

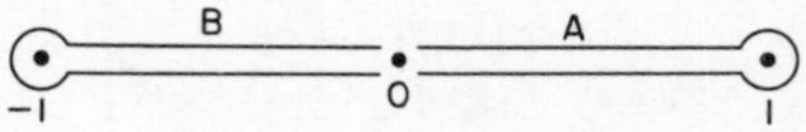

FIG. 2.

On traversing loop $A$ in the positive sense, the straight pieces have no effect on $f(z)$ since they do not contain a branch point. Traversing the small circle round $z = 1$ changes $\arg(z-1)$ by $2\pi$ and hence $\arg \sqrt{(z-1)}$ by $\pi$, so this changes the sign of $f(z)$. To find the effect on $I$ of traversing loop $A$, if $\rho$ is the radius of the small circle, the integrand behaves like $\rho^{-\frac{1}{2}}$ and the length of the path of integration is $2\pi\rho$. Hence $I \sim \rho^{\frac{1}{2}}$ and so $I \to 0$ as $\rho \to 0$. Each edge of the cut contributes the same amount to $I$ and so the contribution of the loop $A$ to $I$ is

$$2 \int_0^1 \frac{dx}{\sqrt{(1-x^2)}} = \pi.$$

The loop $B$ can be similarly discussed and we see that by traversing loops $A$ and $B$ we give the value $2\pi$ to $I$.

20

We readily deduce that if $w$ denotes the value of $I$ taken along any straight path from $O$ to $z$, the general value of $I$ is $m\pi + (-1)^m w$.

If we write

$$w = \int_0^z \frac{dt}{\sqrt{(1-t^2)}},$$

then $z = \sin w$ is the inverse function of the integral and we know that $\sin w$ has the single period $2\pi$ given by

$$2 \int_{-1}^1 \frac{dt}{\sqrt{(1-t^2)}} = 4 \int_0^1 \frac{dt}{\sqrt{(1-t^2)}}.$$

Thus the periodicity of the sine function can be deduced from the periodicity of the above integral $I$.

## 2.2 The Function sn $u$

Now consider

$$J = \int_0^z F(z)\, dz,$$

where

$$F(z) = \{(1-z^2)(1-k^2 z^2)\}^{-\frac{1}{2}} \quad \text{and} \quad 0 < k < 1.$$

We outline now the method of discussing $J$ on the same lines as we have discussed $I$. The branch points now are $\pm 1$, $\pm 1/k$. For the branch points $\pm 1$ we have two loops $A$ and $B$ similar to the previous case. The loop $A$, from 0 to 1, gives to $J$ the value $2K$, where

$$K = \int_0^1 \frac{dx}{\sqrt{\{(1-x^2)(1-k^2 x^2)\}}},$$

and the integrand returns to 0 with the value $-1$, the initial value of $F(z)$ having been chosen to be $+1$.

Since $1/k > 1$, loops $L_1$ and $L_2$ round the branch points $\pm 1/k$ can be deformed into contours which pass through the points $\pm 1$ as illustrated for $L_1$ in Fig. 3. We take a small semicircle round 1 and a small circle round $1/k$, both of radius $\varepsilon$. It is easy to show that the integrals round the semicircle and round the circle tend to zero as $\varepsilon \to 0$. The integral from 0 to $1-\varepsilon$ along $Ox$ as $\varepsilon \to 0$ gives $K$; the integral from $1+\varepsilon$ to $(1/k)-\varepsilon$ as $\varepsilon \to 0$ gives $iK'$, where

$$K' = \int\limits_{1}^{1/k} \frac{dx}{\sqrt{\{(x^2-1)(1-k^2x^2)\}}}$$

or

$$iK' = \int\limits_{1}^{1/k} \frac{dx}{\sqrt{\{(1-x^2)(1-k^2x^2)\}}}.$$

Thus the contribution to $J$ of traversing the loop $L_1$ from 0 to $1/k$ is $2K+2iK'$ and $F(z)$ returns to 0 with the value $-1$.

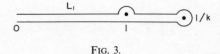

FIG. 3.

In a similar manner we can discuss the loop $L_2$ from 0 to $-1/k$ and show that the contribution to $J$ of traversing $L_2$ is $-2K-2iK'$.
If now $w$ denotes the value of

$$\int\limits_{0}^{z} F(t)\,dt$$

taken along a straight line from 0 to $z$, with the initial value $+1$ at 0, the general value of $J$ is

$$2mK + 2niK' + (-1)^m w,$$

where $m$ and $n$ are integers.
In the case of

$$w = \int\limits_{0}^{z} (1-t^2)^{-\frac{1}{2}}\,dt$$

we have seen that the inverse function $z = \sin w$ has the same period $2\pi$ as the integral. But we know that the sine function is one-valued. If now

$$w = \int_0^z \frac{dt}{\sqrt{\{(1-t^2)(1-k^2t^2)\}}},$$

$z$ can be regarded as a function of $w$, but we do not know, without proof, that the inverse function $z(w)$ is one-valued. The proof that it is one-valued can be made to depend on the existence theorem in differential equations that, if $\phi(z)$ is one-valued, $dz/dw = \phi(z)$ has a single-valued solution if an initial condition is given. For brevity we shall omit this proof and assume that the inverse function of the above integral exists for all values of $w$ and that it is one-valued. We denote the function so defined by $z = \operatorname{sn} w$.

It follows from the periods of the integral discussed above that

$$\operatorname{sn} w = \operatorname{sn}\{2mK + 2niK' + (-1)^m w\}$$

so that sn $w$ has the two periods $4K$, $4iK'$, one real and one complex. It also follows that sn $w$ is an odd function for

$$\int_0^{-z} F(t)\, dt = -\int_0^z F(t)\, dt = -w,$$

$$-z = \operatorname{sn}(-w) = -\operatorname{sn} w.$$

In this way we define the first of the three Jacobian E.F., sn $w$. The function just defined as the inverse of an integral has been shown to be d.p. To establish that it is an E.F. it is necessary to show also that it is meromorphic. It is very difficult to prove that the integral formula defines $z$ as a meromorphic function of $w$ with simple poles. It is easier to do this if we define sn $w$ in terms of some functions known as Theta functions.† Alternatively, sn $u$ can be defined in terms of $\wp(u)$ by means of formulae, proved later in § 2.11, when its poles can be found in terms of those of $\wp(u)$.

### 2.3 The Constants $K$ and $K'$

Since

$$iK' = \int_1^{1/k} \frac{dt}{\sqrt{\{(1-t^2)(1-k^2t^2)\}}},$$

† See Whittaker and Watson, *Modern Analysis*, Ch. XXI and p. 492 for the definition of sn $u$.

if we make the transformation $1/u = \sqrt{(1-k'^2t^2)}$, where $k'^2 = 1-k^2$, we readily see that

$$K' = \int_0^1 \frac{du}{\sqrt{\{(1-u^2)(1-k'^2u^2)\}}}$$

so that $K'$ is the same function of $k'$ as $K$ is of $k$. We call $k$ the *modulus* and $k'$ the *complementary modulus* of the Jacobian E.F.

We have also

$$K+iK' = \int_0^{1/k} \frac{dt}{\sqrt{\{(1-t^2)(1-k^2t^2)\}}},$$

$$K'+iK = \int_0^{1/k'} \frac{dt}{\sqrt{\{(1-t^2)(1-k'^2t^2)\}}}.$$

### 2.4 The Functions cn $u$, dn $u$

Having defined sn $u$, we can now define the other two Jacobian E.F. as follows: cn $u = \sqrt{(1-\mathrm{sn}^2u)}$, dn $u = \sqrt{(1-k^2\,\mathrm{sn}^2u)}$.

Since

$$u = \int_0^{\mathrm{sn}\,u} \frac{dt}{\sqrt{\{(1-t^2)(1-k^2t^2)\}}}$$

we have, on differentiation,

$$1 = \frac{\mathrm{sn}'u}{\sqrt{\{(1-\mathrm{sn}^2u)(1-k^2\,\mathrm{sn}^2u)\}}},$$

so that $\mathrm{sn}'u = \mathrm{cn}\,u\,\mathrm{dn}\,u$.

From this we deduce that cn $u$, dn $u$ are one-valued if their initial values are determined. Since sn $u$ is one-valued so is sn$'u$, hence cn $u$, dn $u$, if they change in value at all, must do so together. But this is impossible as the only points which may be branch points of cn $u$ are where $\mathrm{sn}^2u = 1$ and for dn $u$ those where $\mathrm{sn}^2u = 1/k^2$, and $\mathrm{sn}^2u$ cannot be both 1 and $1/k^2$ at the same point. We fix the initial values by taking cn $u$ and dn $u$ both $+1$ when $u = 0$.

We easily obtain, by direct differentiation, that

$$\text{cn}'u = -\text{sn } u \text{ dn } u, \quad \text{d}n'u = -k^2 \text{ sn } u \text{ cn } u.$$

## 2.5 The Addition Theorems

NOTATION: *In any formula involving* sn *u and* sn *v, we usually write these* $s_1, s_2$ *and similarly for* cn *u,* dn *u. We also write S for* sn 2u. *Another notation commonly used is to write* ns *u for* 1/sn *u, etc.*

The addition theorem for the sn function is

$$\text{sn}(u+v) = \frac{\text{sn } u \text{ cn } v \text{ dn } v + \text{ sn } v \text{ cn } u \text{ dn } u}{1 - k^2 \text{ sn}^2 u \text{ sn}^2 v}. \tag{1}$$

We write the denominator of this expression as $\Delta$ and the three addition theorems in abbreviated notation are:

$$\text{sn}(u+v) = \frac{s_1 c_2 d_2 + s_2 c_1 d_1}{\Delta}, \quad \text{cn}(u+v) = \frac{c_1 c_2 - s_1 s_2 d_1 d_2}{\Delta},$$

$$\text{dn}(u+v) = \frac{d_1 d_2 - k^2 s_1 s_2 c_1 c_2}{\Delta}.$$

To prove (1) call the right-hand side $F(u, v)$: then, by direct differentiation, we can show that†

$$\frac{\partial F}{\partial u} = \frac{\partial F}{\partial v}.$$

If $G(u, v) = u + v$ then clearly

$$\frac{\partial(F, G)}{\partial(u, v)} = \begin{vmatrix} \dfrac{\partial F}{\partial u} & \dfrac{\partial F}{\partial v} \\ 1 & 1 \end{vmatrix} = 0,$$

so there is a functional relation between $F$ and $G$ so we can write

$$F = \phi(G) = \phi(u + v).$$

On putting $v = 0$ we find that $\phi(u) = \text{sn } u$, whence the right-hand side of (1) is equal to $\text{sn}(u + v)$.

The addition theorems for cn and dn can be proved similarly. Other methods of proof can be given. One method makes use of the comparison theorems of § 1.4 and will be given in § 2.11.

---

† The reader should prove this result as an exercise.

3

## 2.6 Periodicity

By means of the addition theorems we readily verify the periodicity of the Jacobian E.F. The periods are shown in Table 1.

TABLE 1

| With respect to | sn $u$ | cn $u$ | dn $u$ |
|---|---|---|---|
| $K$ | $4K$ | $4K$ | $2K$ |
| $iK'$ | $2iK'$ | $4iK'$ | $4iK'$ |
| $K+iK'$ | $4K+4iK'$ | $2K+2iK'$ | $4K+4iK'$ |

We observe that, in each column, one of the periods is a multiple of 2 only, the other two are multiples of 4. So from the above we choose pairs of *primitive periods*. For sn $u$, $4K$, $2iK'$; cn $u$, $4K$, $2K+2iK'$; dn $u$, $2K$, $4iK'$.

Each of the Jacobian E.F. takes every value twice in a p.p. A region in which they take any value exactly once is called a *fundamental region*, so a fundamental region is half a p.p.

We can represent the p.p. for the three Jacobian functions diagrammatically, marking zeros by ° and poles by *. The fundamental regions are shaded.

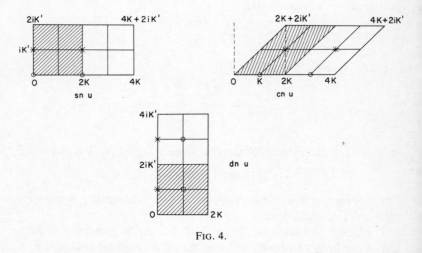

FIG. 4.

We note that all three Jacobian functions have a pole at $iK'$. These poles are simple poles with residues $i/k$, $-i/k$, $-i$ respectively.

Each Jacobian E.F. has two distinct zeros and two distinct poles in a p.p. as is evident from the above diagrams.

## 2.7 Expansions in Powers of $u$

Each of these can be determined by Taylor's theorem.

$$\text{sn}\, u = \text{sn}0 + u\, \text{sn}'0 + \frac{u^2}{2!}\, \text{sn}''0 + \ldots$$

Since $\text{sn}'u = \text{cn}\, u\, \text{dn}\, u$, $\text{sn}''u = -\text{sn}\, u\, \text{dn}^2u - k^2\, \text{sn}\, u\, \text{cn}^2u$,
$\text{sn}'''u = -\text{cn}\, u\, \text{dn}^3u + 2k^2\, \text{sn}^2u\, \text{cn}\, u\, \text{dn}\, u$

$$-k^2\, \text{cn}^3u\, \text{dn}\, u + 2k^2\, \text{sn}^2u\, \text{cn}\, u\, \text{dn}\, u,$$

we see that $\text{sn}0 = 0$, $\text{sn}'0 = 1$, $\text{sn}''0 = 0$, $\text{sn}'''0 = -(1+k^2)$, and so on; thus

$$\text{sn}\, u = u - \frac{u^3}{3!}(1+k^2) + (1+4k^2+k^4)\frac{u^5}{5!} + \ldots$$

Similarly

$$\text{cn}\, u = 1 - \frac{u^2}{2!} + \frac{u^4}{4!}(1+4k^2) - \ldots,$$

$$\text{dn}\, u = 1 - \frac{k^2u^2}{2!} + \frac{u^4}{4!}k^2(k^2+4) - \ldots$$

These series are all valid for $|u| < K'$, since the nearest singularity of each of the functions to the origin is $u = iK'$.

In the degenerate case when $k = 0$, we see that $\text{sn}\, u$ becomes $\sin u$, $\text{cn}\, u$ becomes $\cos u$ and $\text{dn}\, u$ is 1. These results are useful for verifying formulae in Jacobian E.F. The above series converge only slowly and are not much use for numerical calculation. For numerical calculation it is better to use theta functions.† One of the methods of defining the Jacobian E.F. is by means of the theta functions, as stated earlier.

## 2.8 Identities and Duplication Formulae

The standard method of establishing identities in Jacobian E.F. is to express everything in terms of the sn function. If the original

† See, e.g., Whittaker and Watson, *Modern Analysis*, Ch. XXI.

identity holds the result will be an algebraical identity in $s_1, s_2, \ldots$ and there is no more appeal to the theory of E.F.

EXAMPLE. Show that

$$\frac{s_1 c_2 d_2 + s_2 c_1 d_1}{1 - k^2 s_1^2 s_2^2} = \frac{s_1 c_2 d_1 + s_2 c_1 d_2}{d_1 d_2 + k^2 s_1 c_1 s_2 c_2}.$$

Assume that the identity holds; multiply across and the left-hand side is

$$s_1 c_2 d_1 d_2^2 + k^2 s_1^2 s_2 c_1 c_2^2 d_2 + s_2 c_1 d_1^2 d_2 + k^2 s_1 s_2^2 c_1^2 c_2 d_1$$
$$= s_1 c_2 d_1 (1 - k^2 s_2^2) + k^2 s_1^2 s_2 c_1 d_2 (1 - s_2^2) + s_2 c_1 d_2 (1 - k^2 s_1^2)$$
$$+ k^2 s_1 s_2^2 c_2 d_1 (1 - s_1^2).$$

By a little rearrangement this is equivalent to the right-hand side

$$(1 - k^2 s_1^2 s_2^2)(s_1 c_2 d_1 + s_2 c_1 d_2).$$

This method is rarely the best one. More complicated identities are best established by means of the addition and duplication theorems.

## Some Duplication Formulae

By putting $u = v$ in the addition theorems we get at once

$$S = \frac{2scd}{1 - k^2 s^4}, \qquad C = \frac{1 - 2s^2 + k^2 s^4}{1 - k^2 s^4}, \qquad D = \frac{1 - 2k^2 s^2 + k^2 s^4}{1 - k^2 s^4},$$

and from these, by rearrangement, we can deduce that

$$s^2 = \frac{1 - C}{1 + D} = \frac{1}{k^2} \frac{1 - D}{1 + C} = -\frac{1}{k^2} \frac{k'^2 + k^2 C - D}{D - C} = \frac{D - C}{k'^2 - k^2 C + D},$$

$$c^2 = \frac{C + D}{1 + D} = \frac{1}{k^2} \frac{k^2 C + D - k'^2}{1 + C} = \frac{k'^2}{k^2} \frac{1 - D}{D - C} = k'^2 \frac{1 + C}{k'^2 - k^2 C + D},$$

$$d^2 = \frac{C + D}{1 + C} = \frac{k'^2 + k^2 C + D}{1 + D} = k'^2 \frac{1 - C}{D - C} = k'^2 \frac{1 + D}{k'^2 - k^2 C + D}.$$

There are many other such formulae, of course.

## 2.9 Jacobi's "Imaginary" Transformation

A simple relation holds between Jacobian E.F. of argument $iu$ and modulus $k$ and those of argument $u$ and modulus $k'$.

Define a function $v$ of $u$ such that

$$\operatorname{sn} v = i\frac{\operatorname{sn} u}{\operatorname{cn} u}, \tag{1}$$

where $v$ is zero when $u$ is zero. It follows that

$$\operatorname{cn}^2 v = \frac{1}{\operatorname{cn}^2 u}, \quad \operatorname{cn} v = \pm\frac{1}{\operatorname{cn} u},$$

and by putting $u = 0$ we find that the $+$ sign must be taken, so

$$\operatorname{cn} v = \frac{1}{\operatorname{cn} u}. \tag{2}$$

Similarly

$$\operatorname{dn}^2 v = \frac{1 - k'^2 \operatorname{sn}^2 u}{\operatorname{cn}^2 u}.$$

This formula can be simplified by taking the modulus of the $u$-functions to be $k'$, then

$$\operatorname{dn}^2 v = \frac{\operatorname{dn}^2(u, k')}{\operatorname{cn}^2(u, k')}$$

so

$$\operatorname{dn} v = \frac{\operatorname{dn}(u, k')}{\operatorname{cn}(u, k')}, \tag{3}$$

where $(u, k')$ is written because the functions on the right of (3) have modulus $k'$.

Differentiate (2) and we get

$$-\operatorname{dn} v \operatorname{sn} v \, dv = \frac{\operatorname{sn} u \operatorname{dn} u}{\operatorname{cn}^2 u} \, du.$$

On substituting for the $v$-functions we get

$$dv = i \, du,$$

so $v = iu + \text{const.}$, and the constant is zero since $u$ and $v$ vanish together. We have thus established Jacobi's transformation in the three equations

$$\operatorname{sn}(iu, k) = i\frac{\operatorname{sn}(u, k')}{\operatorname{cn}(u, k')},$$

$$\operatorname{cn}(iu, k) = \frac{1}{\operatorname{cn}(u, k')},$$

$$\operatorname{dn}(iu, k) = \frac{\operatorname{dn}(u, k')}{\operatorname{cn}(u, k')}.$$

## 2.10 The Jacobian Functions for Values Connected with the Periods

From the integrals for $K$ and $K+iK'$ in § 2.3 we get at once

$$\operatorname{sn} K = 1, \qquad \operatorname{sn}(K+iK') = 1/k,$$

from which it follows that $\operatorname{cn} K = 0$, $\operatorname{dn} K = \sqrt{(1-k^2)} = \pm k'$. So far $k'$ has only been defined by the equation $k'^2 = 1-k^2$. We now *define* $k'$ to be $\operatorname{dn} K$ to determine the sign of the ambiguity as $+$.

Similarly we get

$$\operatorname{cn}(K+iK') = \sqrt{\left(1-\frac{1}{k^2}\right)} = \pm\frac{ik'}{k}; \qquad \operatorname{dn}(K+iK') = 0.$$

For the moment we leave the sign ambiguous but determine it later.

When $u = iK'$ the value of all three functions is infinite. This is clear from the fact that $\operatorname{sn} iK' = \operatorname{sn}(K+iK'-K)$, and applying the addition theorem we find that the denominator

$$\Delta = 1 - k^2 \operatorname{sn}^2(K+iK')\operatorname{sn}^2 K = 0.$$

We use Jacobi's Imaginary Transformation to ascertain the behaviour of the Jacobian functions in the neighbourhood of $iK'$.

$$\operatorname{sn}(iu+iK', k) = i\frac{\operatorname{sn}(u+K', k')}{\operatorname{cn}(u+K', k')}.$$

Now for functions of modulus $k'$, $K'$ plays the same part that $K$ plays for functions of modulus $k$, so that $\operatorname{sn} K' = 1$ and

$$\operatorname{sn}(u+K', k') = \frac{\operatorname{sn} u \operatorname{cn} K' \operatorname{dn} K' + \operatorname{sn} K' \operatorname{cn} u \operatorname{dn} u}{1 - k'^2 \operatorname{sn}^2 u \operatorname{sn}^2 K'} = \frac{\operatorname{cn}(u, k')}{\operatorname{dn}(u, k')}. \qquad (1)$$

Similarly

$$cn(u+K', k') = -k\frac{sn(u, k')}{dn(u, k')}. \tag{2}$$

From (1) and (2)

$$sn(iu+iK', k) = -\frac{i}{k}\frac{cn(u, k')}{sn(u, k')}$$

and this, by the reversal of Jacobi's transformation, is

$$\frac{1}{k\,sn(iu, k)}.$$

On replacing $iu$ by $u$ we get

$$sn(u+iK', k) = \frac{1}{k\,sn(u, k)},$$

$$cn(u+iK', k) = -\frac{i}{k}\frac{dn(u, k)}{sn(u, k)},$$

$$dn(u+iK', k) = -i\frac{cn(u, k)}{sn(u, k)}.$$

Since the denominators all vanish when $u = 0$ we see that each of the functions has a simple pole at $iK'$; the corresponding residues are $1/k$, $-i/k$, $-i$, as we see if we multiply by $u$, and use the fact that $\lim_{u\to 0}(sn\,u/u) = 1$. We get, on putting $u = K$,

$$sn(K+iK') = 1/k, \quad cn(K+iK') = -ik'/k, \quad dn(K+iK') = 0.$$

This determines the ambiguous sign in $cn(K+iK')$, and it is minus.
  Since

$$sn^2\tfrac{1}{2}K = \frac{1-cn\,K}{1+dn\,K} = \frac{1}{1+k'}$$

we get

$$sn\tfrac{1}{2}K = \pm\frac{1}{\sqrt{(1+k')}}.$$

If we make $k \to 0$ then $K \to \tfrac{1}{2}\pi$ so we determine the ambiguous sign to be $+$, so

$$\text{sn}\tfrac{1}{2}K = \frac{1}{\sqrt{(1+k')}}, \quad \text{cn}\tfrac{1}{2}K = \frac{\sqrt{k'}}{\sqrt{(1+k')}}, \quad \text{dn}\tfrac{1}{2}K = \sqrt{k'}.$$

Using Jacobi's transformation we have

$$\text{sn}\tfrac{1}{2}iK' = i\,\frac{\text{sn}(\tfrac{1}{2}K', k')}{\text{cn}(\tfrac{1}{2}K', k')} = \frac{i/\sqrt{(1+k)}}{\sqrt{k}/\sqrt{(1+k)}} = \frac{i}{\sqrt{k}}.$$

Similarly

$$\text{cn}\tfrac{1}{2}iK' = \frac{\sqrt{(1+k)}}{\sqrt{k}}, \quad \text{dn}\tfrac{1}{2}iK' = \sqrt{(1+k)}.$$

By means of the addition theorems we can then deduce that

$$\text{sn}\tfrac{1}{2}(K+iK') = \frac{1}{\sqrt{(2k)}}\{\sqrt{(1+k)}+i\sqrt{(1-k)}\},$$

$$\text{cn}\tfrac{1}{2}(K+iK') = \frac{1-i}{\sqrt{2}}\frac{\sqrt{k'}}{\sqrt{k}},$$

$$\text{dn}\tfrac{1}{2}(K+iK') = \frac{\sqrt{k'}}{\sqrt{2}}\{\sqrt{(1+k')}-i\sqrt{(1-k')}\}.$$

For quick reference for the values of the functions for arguments which are half and quarter periods, see Table 2.

TABLE 2

| $u+$ | $K$ | $iK'$ | $K+iK'$ | $2K$ | $2iK'$ | $2K+2iK'$ |
|------|-----|-------|---------|------|--------|-----------|
| sn | $\dfrac{\text{cn }u}{\text{dn }u}$ | $\dfrac{1}{k\,\text{sn }u}$ | $\dfrac{\text{dn }u}{k\,\text{cn }u}$ | $-\text{sn }u$ | $\text{sn }u$ | $-\text{sn }u$ |
| cn | $-k'\dfrac{\text{sn }u}{\text{dn }u}$ | $-\dfrac{i}{k}\dfrac{\text{dn }u}{\text{sn }u}$ | $-\dfrac{ik'}{k}\dfrac{1}{\text{cn }u}$ | $-\text{cn }u$ | $-\text{cn }u$ | $\text{cn }u$ |
| dn | $k'\dfrac{1}{\text{dn }u}$ | $-i\dfrac{\text{cn }u}{\text{sn }u}$ | $ik'\dfrac{\text{sn }u}{\text{cn }u}$ | $\text{dn }u$ | $-\text{dn }u$ | $-\text{dn }u$ |
| $0+$ | | | | | | |
| sn | $1$ | $\infty$ | $1/k$ | $0$ | $0$ | $0$ |
| cn | $0$ | $\infty$ | $-ik'/k$ | $-1$ | $-1$ | $1$ |
| dn | $k'$ | $\infty$ | $0$ | $1$ | $-1$ | $-1$ |

## 2.11 Applications of the Method of Comparison to Jacobian Functions

(I) *Expression in terms of $\wp(u)$*

We write $iK'/\omega_2 = K/\omega_1 = c$ and the constant $c$ is to be determined, $k$ having been chosen to make this possible.

Note that we do not put $iK' = \omega_2$, $K = \omega_1$ because $\omega_1$ and $\omega_2$ are arbitrary but $K$ and $K'$ are not; they are functions of $k$ and there is a relation between them. Consider $\wp(u) - e_1$. This has a double pole at the origin so it has two poles in a p.p. It must therefore have two zeros. One is plainly $u = \omega_1$ and using Theorem IV of § 1.2, $\omega_1 + \zeta =$ period, so the unknown zero $\zeta$ is given by $\zeta = -\omega_1$ + period $= \omega_1 +$ period, so both zeros occur at $u = \omega_1$.

Thus $f(u) = \wp(u) - e_1$ is periodic in $2\omega_1$, $2\omega_2$ with double pole at the origin, double zero at $u = \omega_1$. This suggests comparison with $\phi(u) = \mathrm{cn}^2(cu)/\mathrm{sn}^2(cu)$. Since $\mathrm{cn}^2 u = \mathrm{cn}^2(u + 2K) = \mathrm{cn}^2(u + 2c\omega_1)$, $\mathrm{cn}^2(cu) = \mathrm{cn}^2\{c(u + 2\omega_1)\}$ and similarly for $\omega_2$ and $\mathrm{sn}^2(cu)$. Thus $f(u)$ and $\phi(u)$ both have periods $2\omega_1$, $2\omega_2$. Similarly we see that $\phi(u)$ has a double pole at $u = 0$, the same as $f(u)$, and since $\mathrm{cn}^2(cu) = 0$ when $cu = K$, i.e. when $u = \omega_1$, $\phi(u)$ has a double zero at $u = \omega_1$, the same as $f(u)$. By the method of comparison $f(u) = C\phi(u)$. To find $C$ we compare the functions near $u = 0$. Since $\wp(u) - e_1 \sim 1/u^2$ and $\mathrm{cn}^2(cu)/\mathrm{sn}^2(cu) \sim 1/c^2u^2$ we find that the constant must be $c^2$, so

$$\wp(u) - e_1 = c^2 \frac{\mathrm{cn}^2(cu)}{\mathrm{sn}^2(cu)}. \tag{1}$$

In the same way we can show that

$$\wp(u) - e_2 = \frac{c^2}{\mathrm{sn}^2(cu)}, \tag{2}$$

$$\wp(u) - e_3 = c^2 \frac{\mathrm{dn}^2(cu)}{\mathrm{sn}^2(cu)}. \tag{3}$$

If, in eqn. (2), we put $u = \omega_1$, $cu = K$ we get $e_1 - e_2 = c^2$, so $c = \sqrt{(e_1 - e_2)}$. Here we have $k = -\{(e_3 - e_2)/(e_1 - e_2)\}^{\frac{1}{2}}$.

Some writers use (1), (2) and (3) to define the Jacobian E.F.†

(II) *Another proof of the addition theorems*

Compare the functions $f(u) = \mathrm{sn}\, u\, \mathrm{sn}(u + v)$ and $\phi(u) = \mathrm{cn}\, u\, \mathrm{cn}(u + v) - \mathrm{cn}\, v$. Both have periods $2K$, $2iK'$, simple poles at $u = iK'$, $u = -v + iK'$ and simple zeros at $u = 0$ and at $u = -v$, results all easily verified.

† See, e.g., Copson, *Functions of a Complex Variable*, Ch. XIV.

Hence
$$Cf(u) = \phi(u).$$

If $u$ is small we have
$$C = \frac{(1 + Au^2 + \ldots)(\operatorname{cn} v - u \operatorname{sn} v \operatorname{dn} v + \ldots) - \operatorname{cn} v}{u \operatorname{sn} v + \ldots}$$

$$= -\operatorname{dn} v + Bu + \text{higher powers of } u.$$

Hence when $u = 0$, $C = -\operatorname{dn} v$.

Thus
$$\operatorname{cn} u \operatorname{cn}(u+v) + \operatorname{sn} u \operatorname{dn} v \operatorname{sn}(u+v) - \operatorname{cn} v = 0.$$

On interchanging $u$ and $v$,
$$\operatorname{cn} v \operatorname{cn}(u+v) + \operatorname{sn} v \operatorname{dn} u \operatorname{sn}(u+v) - \operatorname{cn} u = 0,$$

two equations from which we can determine both $\operatorname{sn}(u+v)$ and $\operatorname{cn}(u+v)$. Solving for $\operatorname{sn}(u+v)$ we get

$$\operatorname{sn}(u+v) = \frac{c_1^2 - c_2^2}{s_2 c_1 d_1 - s_1 c_2 d_2} = \frac{(s_1^2 - s_2^2)(s_1 c_2 d_2 + s_2 c_1 d_1)}{s_1^2 c_2^2 d_2^2 - s_2^2 c_1^2 d_1^2}$$

$$= \frac{(s_1^2 - s_2^2)(s_1 c_2 d_2 + s_2 c_1 d_1)}{(s_1^2 - s_2^2)(1 - k^2 s_1^2 s_2^2)} = \frac{s_1 c_2 d_2 + s_2 c_1 d_1}{\Delta}.$$

Similarly we can solve for $\operatorname{cn}(u+v)$.

To find $\operatorname{dn}(u+v)$ we compare $f(u)$ with $\psi(u) = \operatorname{dn} u \operatorname{dn}(u+v) - \operatorname{dn} v$. This is left as an exercise for the reader.

## 2.12 The Relation Between Weierstrassian and Jacobian E.F.

Put
$$y = e_3 + \frac{e_1 - e_3}{\operatorname{sn}^2(bu, k)},$$

then, on differentiating and squaring,
$$\left(\frac{dy}{du}\right)^2 = \frac{4b^2(e_1 - e_3)^2 (1 - \operatorname{sn}^2 bu)(1 - k^2 \operatorname{sn}^2 bu)}{\operatorname{sn}^6 bu},$$

$$= \frac{4b^2(e_1 - e_3)^2}{\operatorname{sn}^2 bu}\left(\frac{1}{\operatorname{sn}^2 bu} - 1\right)\left(\frac{1}{\operatorname{sn}^2 bu} - k^2\right),$$

$$= \frac{4b^2}{e_1 - e_3}(y - e_3)(y - e_1)\{y - k^2(e_1 - e_3) - e_3\}.$$

Now put $b^2 = e_1 - e_3$, $k^2 = (e_2 - e_3)/(e_1 - e_3)$ and

$$\left(\frac{dy}{du}\right)^2 = 4(y - e_1)(y - e_2)(y - e_3),$$

so that $y = \wp(u + \lambda)$. Since

$$\wp(u + \lambda) = e_3 + \frac{e_1 - e_3}{\operatorname{sn}^2(bu, k)},$$

on making $u \to 0$ we see that $\lambda$ is a period, since $\lambda$ is then a pole of the $\wp$-function and so of the form $2m\omega_1 + 2n\omega_2$. Hence

$$\wp(u) = e_3 + \frac{e_1 - e_3}{\operatorname{sn}^2(bu, k)},$$

where $b = (e_1 - e_3)^{\frac{1}{2}}$ and $k^2 = (e_2 - e_3)/(e_1 - e_3)$.

This should be compared with the form of the relations in § 2.11.


## 2.13 Elliptic Integrals

Because of their importance in certain applications, we consider briefly Elliptic Integrals.

An integral of the type $\int R(x, \sqrt{X})\, dx$, where $R$ denotes a rational function and $X$ a cubic or quartic in $x$, is called an elliptic integral. The name arose because an integral of this type occurs in the rectification of an ellipse.

An elliptic integral can be expressed as the sum of a finite number of elementary integrals and integrals of the three types:

$$\int \frac{dx}{\sqrt{\{(1 - x^2)(1 - k^2 x^2)\}}}, \quad \int \sqrt{\left(\frac{1 - k^2 x^2}{1 - x^2}\right)}\, dx,$$

$$\int \frac{dx}{(1 + nx^2)\sqrt{\{(1 - x^2)(1 - k^2 x^2)\}}}. \tag{1}$$

On putting $x = \sin\phi$ and taking zero as the lower limit, we get

$$F(k, \phi) = \int_0^\phi \frac{d\phi}{\sqrt{(1 - k^2 \sin^2\phi)}}, \quad E(k, \phi) = \int_0^\phi \sqrt{(1 - k^2 \sin^2\phi)}\, d\phi, \tag{2}$$

$$\Pi(k, \phi) = \int_0^\phi \frac{d\phi}{(1 + n\sin^2\phi)\sqrt{(1 - k^2 \sin^2\phi)}}.$$

These are called elliptic integrals of the first, second and third kinds respectively. If now we put $\sin \phi = \operatorname{sn} u$ we get,

$$F(k, \phi) = u, \quad E(k, \phi) = E(u) = \int_0^u \operatorname{dn}^2 u \, du, \quad \Pi(k, \phi) = \int_0^u \frac{du}{1 + n \operatorname{sn}^2 u}.$$

If the integrals (2) are taken with upper limit $\frac{1}{2}\pi$, they become

$$K = \int_0^1 \frac{dt}{\sqrt{\{(1 - t^2)(1 - k^2 t^2)\}}},$$

$$E = \int_0^{\frac{1}{2}\pi} \sqrt{(1 - k^2 \sin^2 \phi)} \, d\phi = \int_0^K \operatorname{dn}^2 u \, du.$$

We write the first of these integrals $F(k, \frac{1}{2}\pi)$ and the second $E(k, \frac{1}{2}\pi)$ or $E(K)$.

To reduce $\int dx/\sqrt{X}$, where $X$ is a quartic in $x$, to Legendre's standard form, use is made of a substitution due to Cayley. Write

$$X = X_1 X_2 = (ax^2 + 2bx + c)(a'x^2 + 2b'x + c');$$

this we can always do if the coefficients in $X$ are all real, which we are supposing. We then put

$$x = \frac{\lambda t + \mu}{t + 1},$$

choosing $\lambda, \mu$ so that

$$\left. \begin{array}{l} a\lambda\mu + b(\lambda + \mu) + c = 0 \\ a'\lambda\mu + b'(\lambda + \mu) + c' = 0 \end{array} \right\} \tag{3}$$

are satisfied. For brevity, we shall omit the proof that real values of $\lambda$ and $\mu$ can be found to satisfy (3) and illustrate the process by an example.

Consider,

$$I = \int_0^2 \frac{dx}{\{(2x - x^2)(3x^2 + 4)\}^{\frac{1}{2}}}$$

Here $\lambda, \mu$ must satisfy the equations $\lambda + \mu - \lambda\mu = 0$, $3\lambda\mu + 4 = 0$

and choosing the pair $\lambda = -2$, $\mu = \frac{2}{3}$, the transformation is

$$t = \frac{2-3x}{3(x+2)}.$$

Hence

$$I = \sqrt{6} \int_0^{1/3} \frac{dt}{\{(1-9t^2)(1+3t^2)\}^{\frac{1}{2}}}.$$

On putting $3t = u$, then $1-u^2 = w^2$, we get

$$I = \frac{1}{\sqrt{2}} \int_0^1 \frac{dw}{\{(1-w^2)(1-\frac{1}{4}w^2)\}^{\frac{1}{2}}} = \frac{1}{\sqrt{2}} K(\tfrac{1}{2}),$$

and the numerical value of $I$ can be found from tables of $K$. $[K(\tfrac{1}{2}) = 1\cdot6858.]$

The use of Cayley's substitution may not be necessary in every case; sometimes direct algebraic, trigonometrical or hyperbolic substitutions may be more convenient.

## 2.14 The Functions $E(u)$ and $Z(u)$

The integral $E(u)$ has the addition formula

$$E(x+y) = E(x)+E(y)-k^2 \operatorname{sn} x \operatorname{sn} y \operatorname{sn}(x+y), \tag{1}$$

expressed in terms of the arguments $x$ and $y$.

By use of the addition theorems for $\operatorname{dn}(u+v)$, $\operatorname{dn}(u-v)$ we easily get

$$\operatorname{dn}(u+v)+\operatorname{dn}(u-v) = 2d_1 d_2/\Delta,$$

$$\operatorname{dn}(u+v)-\operatorname{dn}(u-v) = -2k^2 s_1 s_2 c_1 c_2/\Delta,$$

whence

$$\operatorname{dn}^2(u+v)-\operatorname{dn}^2(u-v) = -\frac{4k^2 \operatorname{sn} u \operatorname{cn} u \operatorname{dn} u \operatorname{sn} v \operatorname{cn} v \operatorname{dn} v}{(1-k^2 \operatorname{sn}^2 u \operatorname{sn}^2 v)^2};$$

and integration with respect to $v$ gives

$$.E(u+v)+E(u-v) = C - \frac{2 \operatorname{sn} u \operatorname{cn} u \operatorname{dn} u}{\operatorname{sn}^2 u(1-k^2 \operatorname{sn}^2 u \operatorname{sn}^2 v)},$$

where $C$ may depend on $u$ but not on $v$. Put $v = u$, then

$$E(2u) = C - \frac{2 \operatorname{sn} u \operatorname{cn} u \operatorname{dn} u}{\operatorname{sn}^2 u(1 - k^2 \operatorname{sn}^4 u)}.$$

Hence

$$E(u+v) + E(u-v) - E(2u) = \frac{2k^2 \operatorname{sn} u \operatorname{cn} u \operatorname{dn} u}{1 - k^2 \operatorname{sn}^4 u} \cdot \frac{\operatorname{sn}^2 u - \operatorname{sn}^2 v}{1 - k^2 \operatorname{sn}^2 u \operatorname{sn}^2 v},$$

$$= k^2 \operatorname{sn} 2u \operatorname{sn}(u+v) \operatorname{sn}(u-v),$$

and (1) follows by putting $u + v = x$, $u - v = y$.

We define Jacobi's elliptic integral of the second kind by

$$Z(u) = \int_0^u \left( \operatorname{dn}^2 u - \frac{E}{K} \right) du = E(u) - \frac{E}{K} u. \qquad (2)$$

The properties of $Z(u)$ are somewhat simpler than those of $E(u)$. It follows from (1) and (2) that

$$Z(u+v) = Z(u) + Z(v) - k^2 \operatorname{sn} u \operatorname{sn} v \operatorname{sn}(u+v).$$

In particular

$$Z(u+K) = Z(u) - k^2 \operatorname{sn} u \operatorname{cn} u/\operatorname{dn} u,$$

$$Z(u+2K) = Z(u),$$

so we see that $Z(u)$ has the simple period $2K$. The following results are immediate deductions from the above:

$$Z(0) = 0, \qquad Z(K) = 0, \qquad Z(-u) = -Z(u);$$

$$\frac{dZ}{du} = \operatorname{dn}^2 u - \frac{E}{K}, \qquad \frac{d^2 Z}{du^2} = -2k^2 \operatorname{sn} u \operatorname{cn} u \operatorname{dn} u.$$

These results enable us to draw a graph of $Z(u)$, illustrating its simple periodicity in $2K$.

There are, of course, numerous other formulae, but we shall not pursue the investigations any further here.

# Examples 2

**1.** Prove that (i) $\mathrm{sn}(u+v)\,\mathrm{sn}(u-v) = \dfrac{s_1^2 - s_2^2}{\Delta}$,

(ii) $\dfrac{\mathrm{sn}\frac{1}{2}(u+v)\,\mathrm{dn}\frac{1}{2}(u+v)}{\mathrm{cn}\frac{1}{2}(u+v)} = \dfrac{\mathrm{sn}\,u\,\mathrm{dn}\,v + \mathrm{sn}\,v\,\mathrm{dn}\,u}{\mathrm{cn}\,u + \mathrm{cn}\,v}$.

**2.** Prove both by the standard method and by the method of comparison that

$$\frac{1}{\mathrm{cn}(u+v)} + \frac{1}{\mathrm{cn}(u-v)} = \frac{2k^2 c_1 c_2}{d_1^2 d_2^2 - k'^2}.$$

**3.** If

$$F(u, v) = \frac{\mathrm{cn}\,u + \mathrm{cn}\,v}{\mathrm{sn}\,u\,\mathrm{dn}\,v + \mathrm{sn}\,v\,\mathrm{dn}\,u},$$

verify that

$$\frac{\partial F}{\partial u} = \frac{\partial F}{\partial v}$$

and hence deduce that

$$F(u, v) = \frac{1 + \mathrm{cn}(u+v)}{\mathrm{sn}(u+v)}.$$

**4.** Prove that

(i) $\dfrac{1 - \mathrm{dn}\,2u}{1 + \mathrm{dn}\,2u} = \dfrac{k^2 s^2 c^2}{d^2}$,

(ii) $\dfrac{1 + \mathrm{dn}\,2u}{1 - \mathrm{cn}\,2u} = \dfrac{\mathrm{sn}^2 2u}{\mathrm{sn}^2(K - u)}$,

(iii) $\dfrac{\mathrm{cn}(u+v) - \mathrm{dn}(u+v)}{\mathrm{sn}(u+v)} = \dfrac{\mathrm{cn}\,u\,\mathrm{dn}\,v - \mathrm{cn}\,v\,\mathrm{dn}\,u}{\mathrm{sn}\,u - \mathrm{sn}\,v}$.

Deduce from (iii) that if $u + v + w = 2K$,

$$(\mathrm{cn}\,u\,\mathrm{dn}\,v - \mathrm{cn}\,v\,\mathrm{dn}\,u)(\mathrm{cn}\,w - \mathrm{dn}\,w) = k'^2\,\mathrm{sn}\,w(\mathrm{sn}\,u - \mathrm{sn}\,v).$$

**5.** Show that for small values of $u$

$$\mathrm{sn}(u + iK') = \frac{1}{ku} + \frac{1 + k^2}{6k}u + O(u^3)$$

and find similar formulae for $\mathrm{cn}(u + iK')$, $\mathrm{dn}(u + iK')$.

**6.** Express the coordinates of any point on the ellipse $x^2/a^2 + y^2/b^2 = 1$ as $(a\,\mathrm{cn}\,u, b\,\mathrm{sn}\,u)$ and show that the tangents at the points whose parameters are $u+v$, $u-v$ meet at the point $\{a\,\mathrm{cn}\,u/\mathrm{cn}\,v, b\,\mathrm{sn}\,u\,\mathrm{dn}\,v/\mathrm{cn}\,v\}$.

Hence show that the tangents at two variable points, whose parameters differ by a constant $2\lambda$, intersect on the ellipse

$$\frac{x^2\,\mathrm{cn}^2\lambda}{a^2} + y^2\,\frac{\mathrm{sn}^2(\lambda + K)}{b^2} = 1.$$

**7.** (i) By comparing the functions

$$f(z) = \mathrm{dn}\, x\, \mathrm{dn}\, y - \mathrm{dn}\, z\, \mathrm{dn}(x+y+z),$$

$$\phi(z) = \mathrm{sn}\, x\, \mathrm{sn}\, y\, \mathrm{cn}\, z\, \mathrm{cn}(x+y+z) + \mathrm{cn}\, x\, \mathrm{cn}\, y\, \mathrm{sn}(x+y+z)\, \mathrm{sn}\, z,$$

prove that $f(z) = k^2 \phi(z)$.

(ii) Show that

$$\mathrm{sn}\, x\, \mathrm{sn}(y-z) + \mathrm{sn}\, y\, \mathrm{sn}(z-x) + \mathrm{sn}\, z\, \mathrm{sn}(x-y)$$

$$= -k^2 \mathrm{sn}\, x\, \mathrm{sn}\, y\, \mathrm{sn}\, z\, \mathrm{sn}(y-z)\, \mathrm{sn}(z-x)\, \mathrm{sn}(x-y).$$

**8.** By considering the roots of the equation $\mathrm{dn}\, 2u = \mathrm{dn}\, u$ show that

$$\mathrm{dn}\,\frac{2K}{3}\,\mathrm{dn}\,\frac{4iK'}{3}\,\mathrm{dn}\,\frac{2K+4iK'}{3}\,\mathrm{dn}\,\frac{2K-4iK'}{3} = -k'^2.$$

**9.** Prove that

(i)    $\{1+\mathrm{sn}(u+v)\}\{1+\mathrm{sn}(u-v)\} = \dfrac{(\mathrm{cn}\, v + \mathrm{sn}\, u\, \mathrm{dn}\, v)^2}{1 - k^2\, \mathrm{sn}^2 u\, \mathrm{sn}^2 v},$

(ii)    $\sqrt{(1+k')}\, \mathrm{sn}(u+\tfrac{1}{2}K) = \dfrac{k's + cd}{c^2 + k'^2 s^2},$

(iii)    $\mathrm{sn}\, u\, \mathrm{sn}(K-u) = \dfrac{S}{1+D}.$

**10.** (i) Prove that

$$\frac{d}{du}(\mathrm{sn}\, u) = k'^2 \frac{\mathrm{sn}(u+K)}{\mathrm{dn}^2(u+K)}.$$

(ii) Find the limits as $u \to 0$ of

(a)    $\dfrac{\mathrm{sn}^2 u}{1 - \mathrm{cn}\, u\, \mathrm{dn}\, u}$    (b)    $\dfrac{u\, \mathrm{dn}\, u - \mathrm{sn}\, u}{u^2\, \mathrm{sn}\, u}.$

**11.** Prove that

$$\int \frac{\mathrm{cn}\, u}{\mathrm{sn}\, u}\, du = \log \frac{1 - \mathrm{dn}\, u}{\mathrm{sn}\, u}, \qquad \int \frac{\mathrm{dn}\, u}{\mathrm{sn}\, u}\, du = \log \frac{1 - \mathrm{cn}\, u}{\mathrm{sn}\, u},$$

$$\int_0^K \frac{\mathrm{sn}\, u}{1 + \mathrm{cn}\, u}\, du = \log \frac{1+k'}{k'}.$$

**12.** Prove that

(i)    $\mathrm{sn}(u+v)\, \mathrm{dn}(u+w)\{\mathrm{cn}\, u\, \mathrm{cn}\, v - \mathrm{cn}\, w\, \mathrm{cn}(u+v+w)\}$

$$= \mathrm{sn}(u+w)\, \mathrm{dn}(u+v)\{\mathrm{cn}\, u\, \mathrm{cn}\, w - \mathrm{cn}\, v\, \mathrm{cn}(u+v+w)\}.$$

(ii)    $\mathrm{sn}(z+x)\, \mathrm{sn}(z+y)\{1 + k^2\, \mathrm{sn}\, z\, \mathrm{sn}\, y\, \mathrm{sn}(z+x+y)\} = \mathrm{sn}\, x\, \mathrm{sn}\, y + \mathrm{sn}\, z\, \mathrm{sn}(z+x+y).$

**13.** Show that

(i) $$\frac{\text{sn}(x+y)}{1+\text{cn}(x+y)} = \frac{s_1 d_2 + s_2 d_1}{c_1 + c_2} = \frac{c_2 - c_1}{s_1 d_2 - s_2 d_1},$$

(ii) $$\frac{\text{sn}(u+v+w)}{\text{sn }u} = \frac{\text{sn }v\,\text{sn}(u+v) - \text{sn }w\,\text{sn}(u+w)}{\text{sn }v\,\text{sn}(u+w) - \text{sn }w\,\text{sn}(u+v)}.$$

**14.** Prove that

(i) $\{1-(1+k')\,\text{sn }u\,\text{sn}(u+K)\}\{1-(1-k')\,\text{sn }u\,\text{sn}(u+K)\} = \{\text{sn}(u+K)-\text{sn }u\}^2,$

(ii) $\dfrac{d}{du}\{\text{sn }u\,\text{sn}(u+K)\} = \dfrac{1}{k^2}\{\text{dn}^2 u - \text{dn}^2(u+K)\}.$

**15.** If

$$E(u) = \int_0^u \text{dn}^2 u \, du,$$

by differentiating dn $u$ sn $u$/cn $u$, prove that

$$\int_0^u \frac{\text{dn}^2 u}{\text{cn}^2 u} \, du = u + \text{dn }u\,\text{sn }u/\text{cn }u - E(u).$$

**16.** If

$$w = 4\int_1^t \frac{dt}{(15t^2 - 2t - 1)^{\frac{1}{4}}(3t^2 - 2t - 1)^{\frac{1}{4}}},$$

show that

$$t = \frac{\text{dn }w}{2\,\text{cn }w - \text{dn }w} \quad (k = \tfrac{1}{2}).$$

**17.** Prove that

(i) $$\int_0^{\frac{1}{2}\pi} \frac{d\theta}{\sqrt{(\sin\theta)}} = \sqrt{2}K \quad (k = 1/\sqrt{2}),$$

(ii) $$\int_0^{\frac{1}{2}\pi} \sqrt{(\sin\theta)}\,d\theta = \sqrt{2}(2E - K) \quad (k = 1/\sqrt{2}).$$

**18.** By using the addition formulae, prove that

(i) $E(\tfrac{1}{2}k) = \tfrac{1}{2}E + \tfrac{1}{2}(1 - k'),$

(ii) $Z(\tfrac{1}{2}K) = \tfrac{1}{2}(1 - k').$

4

**19.** If

$$E' = \int_0^{\frac{1}{2}\pi} \sqrt{(1 - k'^2 \sin^2\phi)}\, d\phi$$

prove that

$$\frac{dE'}{dk} = \frac{k(K' - E')}{k'^2}.$$

Show also that

$$\frac{dK'}{dk} = \frac{k^2 K' - E'}{kk'^2}.$$

**20.** Prove Legendre's formula,

$$KE' + K'E - KK' = \tfrac{1}{2}\pi.$$

Deduce that, when $k = 1/\sqrt{2}$,

$$E = \frac{1}{2}K + \frac{1}{4}\frac{\pi}{K}.$$

## CHAPTER 3

# CONFORMAL TRANSFORMATION

### 3.1 Ratio of Two Quadratics

This chapter contains some additional results not considered in my previous volume.† We first consider the conformal transformation,

$$w = \frac{az^2 + 2bz + c}{pz^2 + 2qz + r}.$$

This transformation was systematically discussed by Piaggio and Strain‡ in 1947. Special cases of this transformation had previously been used in applications, especially to aerofoil theory, but strangely enough the general case does not appear to have been treated before 1947. A. Cayley considered special cases of this transformation, tracing the bicircular quartics corresponding to $|w| = k$. In the more modern way, we consider the general case thus.

The equation

$$az^2 + 2bz + c - w(pz^2 + 2qz + r) = 0$$

has equal roots in $z$ if

$$(b - wq)^2 = (a - wp)(c - wr). \tag{1}$$

This has equal roots in $w$ only if

$$(2bq - ar - cp)^2 = 4(q^2 - pr)(b^2 - ac),$$

or

$$(ar - cp)^2 = 4(br - cq)(aq - bp). \tag{2}$$

This is the condition that $az^2 + 2bz + c$ and $pz^2 + 2qz + r$ should have a common factor involving $z$; in other words that the transformation should merely be bilinear. If we exclude this, then we

† *P.C.V.*, Ch. II and III.
‡ *J. London Math. Soc.*, XXII, 165.

have only to consider unequal roots, say $w = \alpha$, $w = \beta$ of (1). To $w = \alpha$ correspond two equal values of $z$, say $z = \lambda$, and to $w = \beta$ correspond two equal values, $z = \mu$. Also $\lambda \neq \mu$ since $\alpha \neq \beta$. As some of these values may be infinite, we have these possible cases:

   (i) $\alpha$, $\beta$, $\lambda$, $\mu$ all finite.

   (ii) $\alpha = \infty$, $\beta$, $\lambda$, $\mu$ finite.

   (iii) $\lambda = \infty$, $\alpha$, $\beta$, $\mu$ finite.

   (iv) $\alpha = \lambda = \infty$, $\beta$ and $\mu$ finite.

   (v) $\alpha = \mu = \infty$, $\beta$ and $\lambda$ finite.

The necessary and sufficient conditions for $\alpha$ to be infinite when $\lambda$ is finite, viz. that $pz^2 + 2qz + r$ should be of the form $p\{z + (q/p)\}^2$, are $q^2 = pr$, $p \neq 0$. If $\alpha$ and $\lambda$ are both infinite, the denominator is a mere constant so that $p = q = 0$. If $\lambda$, the double root of

$$az^2 + 2bz + c - \alpha(pz^2 + 2qz + r) = 0,$$

is infinite when $\alpha$ is finite $a - \alpha p = 0$ and $b - \alpha q = 0$ giving $aq = bp$. This condition is also satisfied when $p = 0$ and $q = 0$ and so when both $\alpha$ and $\lambda$ are infinite; it is thus the necessary condition for $\lambda$ to be infinite without reference to the value of $\alpha$. The same condition is necessary for $\mu$ to be infinite. Conversely, if $aq = bp$ there are three possibilities. If $p \neq 0$ then $b = aq/p$ so that

$$w = \frac{a(pz^2 + 2qz) + pc}{p(pz^2 + 2qz + r)} \quad \text{or} \quad w - \frac{a}{p} = \frac{pc - ra}{p(pz^2 + 2qz + r)}$$

and $w = a/p$ corresponds to $z = \infty$ (twice). Hence either $\lambda$ or $\mu$ is infinite while the corresponding value of $w$, $\alpha$ or $\beta$, remains finite. If, however, $p = 0$ then either $a = 0$ (excluded because then the transformation is bilinear) or $q = 0$ giving $w = (az^2 + 2bz + c)/r$, so that to $w = \infty$ corresponds $z = \infty$ (twice), i.e. either $\alpha$ and $\lambda$, or $\beta$ and $\mu$, are both infinite.

To sum up, the five possible standard forms, with the necessary and sufficient conditions for them, are:

$$\frac{w - \beta}{w - \alpha} = k\left(\frac{z - \mu}{z - \lambda}\right)^2; \quad q^2 \neq pr, \quad aq \neq bp,$$

$$w - \beta = k\left(\frac{z - \mu}{z - \lambda}\right)^2; \quad q^2 = pr, \quad aq \neq bp, \quad p \neq 0,$$

$$\frac{w - \beta}{w - \alpha} = k(z - \mu)^2; \quad q^2 \neq pr, \quad aq \neq bp, \quad p \neq 0,$$

$$w - \beta = k(z - \mu)^2; \quad p = 0, \quad q = 0,$$

$$w - \beta = \frac{k}{(z - \lambda)^2}; \quad q^2 = pr, \quad aq = bp, \quad p \neq 0.$$

In all these cases we are assuming that (2) is *not* satisfied, so that the transformation does not degenerate into a bilinear one.

By combining $t = \zeta^2$ with the bilinear transformation, any circle with $\alpha$ and $\beta$ as limiting points corresponds, taken twice, to a circle with $\lambda$ and $\mu$ as limiting points. Of the two arcs into which $\alpha$ and $\beta$ divide a circle through them, each corresponds to a complete circle through $\lambda$ and $\mu$ and these two circles are orthogonal. If $-\frac{1}{2}\pi < \arg(\beta - \alpha) \leq \frac{1}{2}\pi$, and if the circle through $\alpha$ and $\beta$ is such that the arc of it which is described anti-clockwise from $\alpha$ to $\beta$ contains an angle $\theta$, then the interior of this circle corresponds to the two areas which lie inside one and outside another of the two orthogonal circles through $\lambda$ and $\mu$ when $\arg k$ lies between $\theta - \pi$ and $\theta$. Some special cases will be found in Examples 3.

### 3.2 Generalized Joukowski Transformations

The Joukowski aerofoil is referred to in my previous volume† and the special case

$$\frac{w - 2}{w + 2} = \left(\frac{z - 1}{z + 1}\right)^2$$

is there considered. This is clearly also a special case of the type of transformation considered in § 3.1 above. Many of the transformations important in mathematical physics belong to the general class

$$w = z \sum_{r=0}^{\infty} \frac{a_r}{z^r},$$

where the $a_r$ may be complex and $a_0 \neq 0$. We usually take $a_0 = 1$. Suppose that the series converges for $|z| \geq a$ and that $dw/dz$ has no zeros outside the circle $C$ defined by $|z| = a$. Then the transformation is conformal for all $z$ outside $C$. When $z$ describes the circle $C$, $w$ will describe a closed curve $\Gamma$. If $dw/dz$ has a simple zero on $C$, then $\Gamma$ will have a cusp at the corresponding point. Also

† *P.C.V.*, III, § 28, p. 76.

a large circle $C$ in the $z$-plane, with centre the origin, will correspond to a large closed curve $\Gamma$, approximately a circle, in the $w$-plane, and conversely. If we proceed inwards from a point on $C$ along a straight line to the origin, the curve $\Gamma$ corresponding to the part of this line outside $C$ will have a unique tangent at each point. $z$ is thus a single-valued function of $w$ and so expressible by a power series,

$$z = w \sum_{r=0}^{\infty} \frac{b_r}{w^r},$$

for sufficiently large $w$.

If further we use $z = ae^{\zeta}$, the part of the $w$-plane outside $\Gamma$ is mapped on the semi-infinite strip $\xi \geqslant 0, 0 \leqslant \eta < 2\pi$ of the $\zeta$-plane. Hence, if a closed curve can be represented parametrically by

$$u + iv = ae^{i\eta} \sum_{r=0}^{\infty} \frac{a_r}{a^r} e^{-ri\eta},$$

where $a$ is real, $a_r$ complex and $a_0 \neq 0$, we see that it is the curve corresponding to $\xi = 0$ of the family

$$w = ae^{\zeta} \sum_{r=0}^{\infty} \frac{a_r}{a^r} e^{-r\zeta} = z \sum_{r=0}^{\infty} \frac{a_r}{z^r}.$$

Take as an illustration, the special case

$$w = \frac{1}{2} \left\{ \frac{a+b}{a} z + \frac{a(a-b)}{z} \right\}.$$

If $z = ae^{i\theta}$ is the circle $C$, then

$$w = u + iv = \tfrac{1}{2}(a+b)e^{i\theta} + \tfrac{1}{2}(a-b)e^{-i\theta} = a\cos\theta + ib\sin\theta,$$

and the curve $\Gamma$ is an ellipse of semi-axis $a$, $b$ with eccentric angle $\theta$. Taking the transformation in the form $w = z + a^2/z$, then to the circle $|z| = a$ correspond the two sides of a line from $(2a, 0)$ to $(-2a, 0)$ and back. This can also be written†

$$\frac{w+2a}{w-2a} = \left( \frac{z+a}{z-a} \right)^2.$$

Now consider

$$\frac{dw}{dz} = \prod_{r=1}^{n} \left( 1 - \frac{z_r}{z} \right),$$

† If $a = -1$ this is the special case referred to in *P.C.V.*, § 28.

where $\Sigma z_r = 0$, $|z_1| = a$, $|z_r| < a$ if $r \neq 1$. Then $\Gamma$ has a cusp at $w_1$; for near it we have $dw/dz = f(z)(z-z_1)$, where $f(z)$ is regular and not zero at $z = z_1$, and so

$$w - w_1 = \tfrac{1}{2} f(z_1)(z - z_1)^2 + \dots$$

Hence, as $z$ travels around the circle $C$ and passes through $z_1$, $w$ approaches $w_1$ and then recedes along a curve with the same tangent. On putting

$$n = 2, \quad z_1 = a, \quad z_2 = -a, \quad \frac{dw}{dz} = 1 - \frac{a^2}{z^2}, \quad w = z + \frac{a^2}{z},$$

we obtain the special case considered above.

If now instead of the circle $C$ we take a slightly larger circle passing through $z = a$ but slightly beyond $z = -a$ and transform it, we get a figure with a cusp at $w = 2a$ and a rounded end at $w$ a little less than $-2a$.†

## Glauert's Modification

All Joukowski aerofoils have a cusp, whereas the trailing edge of an aeroplane wing is not a cusp. A modification, due to Glauert, remedied this. Take

$$\frac{w - (2-n)a \cos \beta}{w + (2-n)a \cos \beta} = \left( \frac{z - ae^{-i\beta}}{z + ae^{i\beta}} \right)^{2-n},$$

where $n$ and $\beta$ are small and positive. Write

$$\arg(z - ae^{-i\beta}) = \theta_1, \qquad\qquad \arg(z + ae^{i\beta}) = \theta_2,$$

$$\arg\{w - (2-n)a \cos \beta\} = \phi_1, \quad \arg\{w + (2-n)a \cos \beta\} = \phi_2,$$

where $\theta_1$, $\theta_2$, $\phi_1$, $\phi_2$ are defined to be zero when $z$ is on $BA$ produced and vary continuously as $z$ travels on a curve outside the circle. Then $\phi_1 - \phi_2 = (2-n)(\theta_1 - \theta_2)$ for points outside $C$. At $P$, $\theta_1 - \theta_2 = \tfrac{1}{2}\pi - \beta$. If $P$ transforms to $\bar{P}$, $\bar{P}$ is on a circular arc through $\pm(2-n)a \cos \beta$ with angle $\lambda = (2-n)(\tfrac{1}{2}\pi - \beta)$ at the circumference. But if $P$ moves to near $B$ and then travels round a small semicircle about $B$, $\theta_2$ increases by $\pi$ and thus $\phi_1 - \phi_2$ becomes

$$(2-n)(\tfrac{1}{2}\pi - \beta) - (2-n)\pi = -(2-n)(\tfrac{1}{2}\pi + \beta).$$

† See Fig. 11, *P.C.V.*, p. 77. In this figure $a = -1$.

Since this is negative, we add $2\pi$ to give a positive angle; then the lower arc of $C$ gives an arc in the $w$-plane containing an angle $2\pi - (2-n)(\frac{1}{2}\pi + \beta) = \mu$. If $\mu < \pi$ the lower arc in the $w$-plane is concave downwards. The figure in the $w$-plane consists of two circular arcs intersecting at an angle $n\pi$.

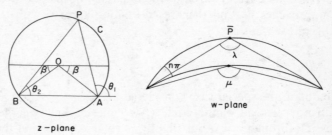

$z$-plane

$w$-plane

FIG. 5.

By taking, instead of $C$, a circle through $A$ but passing a little beyond $B$, we get a rounded leading edge. When $z$ is large it can be shown that the first few terms of the series for $w$ are

$$w = z + ia \sin \beta + \frac{(1-n)(3-n)}{3} \cos^2 \beta \frac{a^2}{z} + \dots$$

### 3.3 Boundary a Closed Polygon

Consider

$$\frac{dw}{dz} = A \prod_{r=1}^{n} \left(1 - \frac{z_r}{z}\right)^{\alpha_r/\pi}, \tag{1}$$

where $A$ is constant and $|z_r| = a$ for all $r$. Put $z = ae^{i\theta}$, $z_r = ae^{i\theta_r}$, then

$$\frac{dw}{d\theta} = Be^{ik\theta} \prod_{r=1}^{n} \{\sin \tfrac{1}{2}(\theta - \theta_r)\}^{\alpha_r/\pi},$$

where $k = 1 - (1/2\pi)\Sigma\alpha_r$ and $B$ is another constant. This follows because

$$e^{i\theta} - e^{i\theta_r} = \cos \theta + i \sin \theta - (\cos \theta_r + i \sin \theta_r),$$

$$= -2 \sin \frac{\theta + \theta_r}{2} \sin \frac{\theta - \theta_r}{2} + 2i \sin \frac{\theta - \theta_r}{2} \cos \frac{\theta + \theta_r}{2},$$

$$= 2i \sin \frac{\theta - \theta_r}{2} e^{\frac{1}{2}i(\theta + \theta_r)};$$

and

$$\frac{dw}{d\theta} = \frac{dw}{dz} \cdot \frac{dz}{d\theta} = iae^{i\theta}\frac{dw}{dz}.$$

If $\Sigma\alpha_r = 2\pi$, $k = 0$ so $\arg(dw/d\theta)$ is constant. Hence as $z$ describes the arc between $z_r$ and $z_{r+1}$, $w$ proceeds along a straight line. When we pass half way round $z_r$, however, $\theta - \theta_r$ changes sign and so $\arg(dw/d\theta)$ changes by $\pm\alpha_r$. The curve $\Gamma$ is thus a polygon with external angles $\pm\alpha_r$.

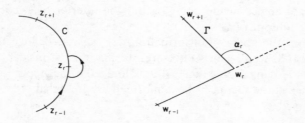

FIG. 6.

If $z$ travels positively about $z_r$, $\arg(z - z_r)$ *increases* by $\pi$. Hence the curves are oriented as shown in Fig. 6. The condition $\Sigma\alpha_r = 2\pi$ is satisfied by the external angles of a closed polygon. If (1) is expanded in powers of $1/z$, it is seen to contain terms of the type

$$\frac{\alpha_r z_r}{z}$$

and hence $w$ will not be one-valued unless $\Sigma\alpha_r z_r = 0$. Subject to this condition, and $\Sigma\alpha_r = 2\pi$, the outside of a circle $C$ is transformed into the outside of a polygon.

The same transformation will not do for the *inside* of a polygon. For if we took the inside of the circle we should have to pass round $z_r$ in the negative sense and $\arg(dw/d\theta)$ would decrease by $\alpha_r$. Thus we should not get the inside of the same polygon, but the outside of its mirror image.

The necessary modification is easily obtained. In brief, we take

$$\frac{dw}{dz} = A \prod_{r=1}^{n}\left(1 - \frac{z}{z_r}\right)^{-\alpha_r/\pi}, \quad \text{where } |z_r| = a. \tag{2}$$

As before

$$\frac{dw}{d\theta} = iae^{i\theta}Ae^{-\frac{1}{2}i\lambda}\prod\{-2i\sin\tfrac{1}{2}(\theta-\theta_r)\}^{-\alpha_r/\pi},$$

where

$$\lambda = \sum\alpha_r(\theta-\theta_r)/\pi.$$

$\text{Arg}(dw/d\theta)$ is constant for each arc provided $\Sigma\alpha_r = 2\pi$. But now, as $z$ describes a semicircle about $z_r$ on the *inside*, $\arg(z-z_r)$ *decreases* by $\pi$ and $\arg(dw/d\theta)$ increases by $\alpha_r$. Thus the $\alpha_r$ are still the external angles of the polygon, but the interior of $C$ corresponds to the interior of $\Gamma$.

From the above transformation, (2), we can deduce the better known Schwarz–Christoffel transformation. Consider a set of points $t_r$ lying along the real axis and take the upper half of the $t$-plane as the region to be conformally represented.

Consider

$$\frac{dw}{dt} = A\prod(t-t_r)^{-\alpha_r/\pi}. \tag{3}$$

When $t$ travels, in the negative sense, around $t_r$, $\arg(dw/dt)$ increases by $\alpha_r$. If $\Sigma\alpha_r = 2\pi$ we get the interior of a closed polygon mapped on the upper half of the $t$-plane. If $\Sigma\alpha_r = \pi$ two sides are parallel and extend to infinity. To see the relation to (2) write,

$$z+ia = \frac{2a^2}{t-ia} \quad\text{or}\quad z = -ia\frac{t+ia}{t-ia}.$$

We get

$$\frac{dw}{dt} = -\frac{2a^2A}{(t-ia)^2}\prod\left\{\frac{2ia(t-t_r)}{(t-ia)(t_r+ia)}\right\}^{-\alpha_r/\pi},$$

$$= C\prod(t-t_r)^{-\alpha_r/\pi},$$

since $\Sigma\alpha_r = 2\pi$.†

This is of exactly the same form as (3); the only difference is that the $t_r$ are on the real axis and the $z_r$ on the circle.

---

† This follows since $[1/(t-ia)^2]\Pi(t-ia)^{\alpha_r/\pi} = [1/(t-ia)^2](t-ia)^{\Sigma\alpha_r/\pi} = 1$ since $\Sigma\alpha_r/\pi = 2$.

### 3.4 Schwarz–Christoffel Transformation

To discuss this directly, without deducing it from the more general discussion of § 3.3, consider a polygon in the $w$-plane with $n$ sides and interior angles $\alpha\pi, \beta\pi, \ldots, \kappa\pi$, where $\alpha + \beta + \ldots + \kappa = n - 2$. If every $\alpha, \beta, \ldots < 1$ the polygon is convex. Some of the $\alpha, \beta, \ldots$ may be greater than 1, but the polygon must not cross itself. Suppose that the vertices of the polygon are to correspond to the $n$ points $a, b, \ldots, k$ on the real axis of the $z$-plane. So long as $z$ remains on the real axis, without passing through any of the points $a, b, \ldots, k$, $w$ remains on the same side of the polygon; and so the angle between the curves in the $z$-plane and $w$-plane is constant, i.e. $\arg(dw/dz)$ is constant.

If

$$\frac{dw}{dz} = C(z-a)^{\alpha-1}(z-b)^{\beta-1}\ldots(z-k)^{\kappa-1},$$

then $\arg(dw/dz)$ is constant. If $z$ passes the point $a$ by a small semicircle above it, $\arg(z-a)$ decreases from $\pi$ to 0, the arguments of the other factors remain unchanged, so $\arg(dw/dz)$ decreases by $\pi(\alpha-1)$. Hence the curve in the $w$-plane turns through the angle $\pi(1-\alpha)$ in the positive sense. This corresponds to an angle $\pi\alpha$ of the polygon.

Hence

$$w = C \int_{z_0}^{z} (t-a)^{\alpha-1}(t-b)^{\beta-1}\ldots(t-k)^{\kappa-1}\, dt,$$

where the constant $C$ may be complex.

As $|t| \to \infty$ the integrand is $O(1/|t|^2)$ so the integral converges as $z \to \pm\infty$, to the same value in each case, since the integral along a large semicircle above the real axis tends to 0. As $z$ describes the real axis, $w$ describes a closed polygon with the prescribed angles. If we consider the real $z$-axis as closed by a large semicircle above it, we find that the interior of the polygon is represented on the upper half-plane.†

It is somewhat difficult to prove that we can choose the constants so that a polygon with given sides as well as given angles can be represented. The result can be verified for a triangle, as follows.

Consider the isosceles right-angled triangle, with vertices $w = i, 0, 1$, and let the vertices correspond to $z = -1, 0, 1$. Since

---

† If $a \to -\infty$ the factor $t-a$ is omitted from the above integral. See *P.C.V.*, p. 80.

the angles of the triangle are $\pi/4$, $\pi/2$, $\pi/4$; $\alpha = \frac{1}{4}$, $\beta = \frac{1}{2}$, $\gamma = \frac{1}{4}$ so we write

$$w = C \int_{z_0}^{z} (t+1)^{-\frac{3}{4}} t^{-\frac{1}{2}} (t-1)^{-\frac{3}{4}} \, dt = C_1 \int_{z_0}^{z} (t+1)^{-\frac{3}{4}} t^{-\frac{1}{2}} (1-t)^{-\frac{3}{4}} \, dt.$$

If $w = 0 \sim z = 0$† we must have $z_0 = 0$. By taking $C_1$ real and positive, the positive directions of the axes correspond. To make $z = 1 \sim w = 1$ we choose $C_1$ so that

$$1 = C_1 \int_{0}^{1} (1-t^2)^{-\frac{3}{4}} t^{-\frac{1}{2}} \, dt, \quad \text{and so } C_1 = 2\sqrt{\pi}/\Gamma^2(\tfrac{1}{4}).$$

EXAMPLE. *Find the transformation which maps the strip of the w-plane, with a cut along the line $v = h$ $(h < \pi)$ extending to $-\infty$. as shown in Fig. 7 on the upper half of the z-plane.*

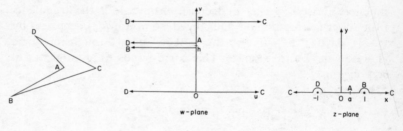

FIG. 7.

The figure in the $w$-plane may be regarded as the limiting form of the quadrilateral $ABCD$ when the angle $A$ becomes $2\pi$ and the other angles zero. For the required Schwarz–Christoffel transformation, $\alpha = 2$, $\beta = \gamma = \delta = 0$. Take the values of $z$ at $D, A, B, C$ to be $-1, a, 1, \infty$, where $a$ is yet to be determined. These points are in the right order if $-1 < a < 1$. The transformation is

$$\frac{dw}{dz} = E(z-1)^{-1}(z-a)(z+1)^{-1},$$

as there is no factor corresponding to $z = \infty$. Using partial

---

† We use the symbol $\sim$ to denote "corresponds to", when dealing with transformations. It was earlier used to denote "behaves like", but this will cause no confusion.

fractions to integrate this we get

$$w = \tfrac{1}{2}E(1-a)\log(z-1) + \tfrac{1}{2}E(1+a)\log(z+1) + F.$$

If $z$ moves from $-\infty$ to $\infty$ along the real axis, we must cut out the points $z = -1$, $z = 1$ by small semicircles of radii $\rho$ because of the singularities there. Round the semicircle at $D$, $\log(z+1)$ decreases by $\pi i$ and the variation in $\log(z-1)$ tends to zero as $\rho \to 0$. Thus the corresponding $w$-point moves from a position near $D$ on $CD$ to a position near $D$ on $DA$, so that $w$ decreases by $i(\pi - h)$. Hence $i(\pi - h) = \tfrac{1}{2}E(1+a)\pi i$.

By discussing the point $B$ ($z = 1$) similarly we get

$$ih = \tfrac{1}{2}E(1-a)\pi i.$$

Hence $E = 1$ and $a = 1 - (2h/\pi)$.

The value of the constant $F$ comes from the values at $A$, since $w = ih \sim z = a$ so that

$$ih = \tfrac{1}{2}(1-a)\log(a-1) + \tfrac{1}{2}(1+a)\log(a+1) + F,$$

giving $F$.

If the slit is midway between the lines $y = 0$, $y = \pi$ then $h = \tfrac{1}{2}\pi$. The reader can readily verify that then, $a = 0$, $F = 0$ and so

$$w = \tfrac{1}{2}\log(z^2 - 1).$$

The reader may like to consider this transformation also as a combination of $2w = \log\zeta$, $\zeta = z^2 - 1$, so verifying the result in another way.

### 3.5 Transformations Involving Elliptic Functions

(I) $z = \operatorname{sn} w$ where $w = u + iv$.

$$\operatorname{sn}(u+iv) = \frac{\operatorname{sn} u \operatorname{cn} iv \operatorname{dn} iv + \operatorname{sn} iv \operatorname{cn} u \operatorname{dn} u}{1 - k^2 \operatorname{sn}^2 u \operatorname{sn}^2 iv}.$$

If we take the $v$-functions with modulus $k'$, then, by Jacobi's imaginary transformation, § 2.9,

$$z = \frac{\operatorname{sn} u \operatorname{dn} v_1 + i \operatorname{sn} v_1 \operatorname{cn} u \operatorname{dn} u \operatorname{cn} v_1}{\operatorname{cn}^2 v_1 + k^2 \operatorname{sn}^2 u \operatorname{sn}^2 v_1},$$

where $v_1$ is written for $v$ to indicate that the $v$-functions have modulus $k'$. $z$ is real if and only if sn $v_1 = 0$, cn $v_1 = 0$, cn $u = 0$ giving $v = 0+$multiples of $2K'$, $v = K'+$multiples of $2K'$, $u = K$ $+$multiples of $2K$.

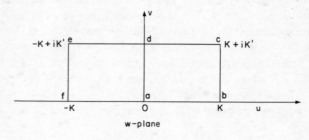

FIG. 8.

Thus $z$ is real when $u+iv$ lies on the rectangle in the figure or on any rectangle obtained from it by repetition. Hence the perimeter of the rectangle corresponds to the real axis in the $z$-plane, corresponding points being denoted by the same letters.

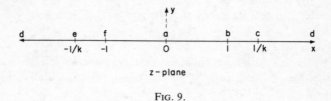

FIG. 9.

Since when $w = \frac{1}{2}iK'$, $z = i/\sqrt{k}$, a point in the upper half $z$-plane, the interior of the rectangle corresponds to the upper half $z$-plane. The arrows on $Ox$ indicate that $d$ is at infinity in the $z$-plane.

To consider whether the transformation is conformal, look at the rectangle $abcd$ of Fig. 8. Since $dz/dw = $ cn $w$ dn $w$, we see that $dz/dw = 0$ at $b$ and $c$ and at $d$, $z = $ sn $w$ has a simple pole. If we cut out the points $b$, $c$ and $d$ then sn $w$ is regular at all other points. The point $w = iK'$ corresponds to the point at infinity on the real axis of the $z$-plane $(d)$.

Since

$$\frac{dw}{dz} = \{(1-z^2)(1-k^2z^2)\}^{-\frac{1}{2}}$$

the transformation can also be considered as a Schwarz–Christoffel type. This is left as an exercise for the reader.

(II) $z = \text{sn}^2 w$. By combining $\zeta = \text{sn } w$ with $z = \zeta^2$ the rectangle *abcd* of Fig. 8 corresponds to the positive real axis of the $z$-plane as illustrated in Fig. 10.

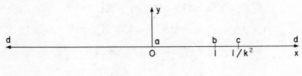

FIG. 10

Corresponding to *abcd* in the $w$-plane we get the positive quadrant of the $\zeta$-plane. Since $\arg z = 2 \arg \zeta$ the positive quadrant of the $\zeta$-plane becomes the upper half $z$-plane.

It is left as an exercise for the reader to discuss what regions of the $z$-plane correspond to the rectangle *abcd* in the $w$-plane by $z = \text{cn } w$ and $z = \text{dn } w$. The results obtained may be checked by reference to (III), where these transformations are considered in more detail.

(III) $z = \text{cn } w$ *and* $z = \text{dn } w$. Consider the rectangle in the $w$-plane with vertices $\pm K$, $\pm K + iK'$.

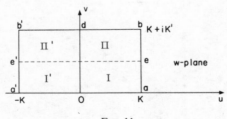

FIG. 11.

If $z = \text{cn } w = \sqrt{(1 - \text{sn}^2 w)}$, $\text{sn}^2 w = (1 - z)(1 + z)$.

If $\zeta = \text{sn } w$ the line *ee'* in the figure is $v = \frac{1}{2}K'$. On this line $\zeta = \text{sn}(u + \frac{1}{2}iK')$ and, on using the addition theorem and the table in §2.10.

$$\zeta = \xi + i\eta = \frac{(1+k)\,\text{sn } u + i \,\text{cn } u \,\text{dn } u}{\sqrt{k(1 + k \,\text{sn}^2 u)}}.$$

It follows that $\xi^2 + \eta^2 = 1/k$ so the line $v = \frac{1}{2}K' \sim$ the circle $|\zeta| = 1/\sqrt{k}$ so $|\zeta|^2 = |\mathrm{sn}\, w|^2 = 1/k$.

Thus the line-segment $e'e$ corresponds to the part of the Cassinian oval $|z-1||z+1| = 1/k$ for which $x \geqslant 0$. The following points correspond:

$$e: \; w = K + \tfrac{1}{2}iK' \sim y = -(1-k)^{\frac{1}{2}}k^{-\frac{1}{2}};$$

$$e': \; w = -K + \tfrac{1}{2}iK' \sim y = (1-k)^{\frac{1}{2}}k^{-\frac{1}{2}};$$

$$b: \; w = K + iK' \sim z = -ik'/k;$$

$$b': \; w = -K + iK' \sim z = ik'/k;$$

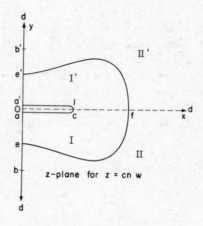

Fig. 12.

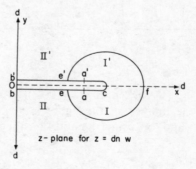

Fig. 13.

Regions which correspond are marked by Roman figures I, II, I', II'. Similarly discussing $z = \mathrm{dn}\, w = \sqrt{(1 - k^2\, \mathrm{sn}^2 w)}$ we find that the line-segment $v = \frac{1}{2}K'$, $-K < u < K$, which is the line $e'e$ in Fig. 11, corresponds to the part $x \geqslant 0$ of the Cassinian oval $|z + 1||z - 1| = k$.

$e$ and $e'$ are $x = \sqrt{(1 - k)}$; $a$ and $a'$ are $x = k'$; $f$ is $x = \sqrt{(1 + k)}$ and $c$ is $x = 1$. See Fig. 13.

(IV) *Interior of Ellipse on Interior of Circle.* In *P.C.V.*, § 26 it was stated that the transformation which maps the interior of an ellipse on the interior of a unit circle involves E.F. We now discuss this problem.

Consider first the transformation $w = \sqrt{k}\, \mathrm{sn}\, \zeta$. This, with $w$ and $\zeta$ interchanged, was discussed in (III) above and we saw that the circle in the $w$-plane $\sim$ the lines $\eta = \pm\frac{1}{2}K'$ in the $\zeta$-plane. On writing $\zeta = 2Kz/\pi$, these are the lines $y = \pi K'/4K$ in the $z$-plane. When $y = \pi K'/4K$, and $x$ is between $\frac{1}{2}\pi$ and $-\frac{1}{2}\pi$, then $u > 0$ as $v$ varies from 1 to $-1$, so the actual curve which corresponds to the line $y = \pi K'/4K$ is half the circumference of the circle with $v > 0$. Similarly the line $y = -\pi K'/4K$ corresponds to the lower half of the circumference.

Now consider in the $z$-plane a rectangle with sides $x = \pm\frac{1}{2}\pi$, $y = \pm\pi K'/4K$. The $w$-curve $\sim x = \frac{1}{2}\pi$, or $\xi = K$, is given by

$$v = 0, \quad u = \sqrt{k}\,\frac{\mathrm{cn}\, i\eta}{\mathrm{dn}\, i\eta}.$$

As $\eta$ varies from $\frac{1}{2}K'$ through 0 to $-\frac{1}{2}K'$, $u$ varies from 1 to $\sqrt{k}$ and back from $\sqrt{k}$ to 1. Hence the rectangle in the $z$-plane $\sim$ the unit circle in the $w$-plane, with two cuts from the circumference inwards, each to a distance $\sqrt{k}$ from the centre.

If now we write $z = c \sin \zeta$ we know, by *P.C.V.*, § 27, that the cut circle in the $w$-plane corresponds to the ellipse $x^2/a^2 + y^2/b^2 = 1$, where

$$a = c \cosh\frac{\pi K'}{4K}, \quad b = c \sinh\frac{\pi K'}{4K},$$

with corresponding cuts. It follows that

$$w = \sqrt{k}\, \mathrm{sn}\left\{\frac{2K}{\pi} \sin^{-1}\frac{z}{c}\right\},$$

where $c^2 = a^2 - b^2$, maps the inside of the ellipse on the inside of the unit circle in the $w$-plane, with the relation holding

$$\left(\frac{a-b}{a+b}\right)^2 = \exp\left(-\frac{\pi K'}{K}\right).$$

The cuts are needed for the subsidiary transformation of the rectangle into the circle, but it is easy to see that the cuts may be removed in the direct transformation from the circle to the ellipse. This is similar to the removal of the cuts in the transformation discussed in *P.C.V.*, § 23.

The rectangle in the $z$-plane becomes a square if $K' = 2K$, when $k = (\sqrt{2}-1)^2$.

### 3.6 Note on Transformations Involving E.F.

Since, if $w = \wp(z)$,

$$z = \int_{\infty}^{w} \frac{dt}{\sqrt{(4t^3 - g_2 t - g_3)}},$$

and†

$$\wp(z) = e_3 + \frac{e_1 - e_3}{\operatorname{sn}^2\{z\sqrt{(e_1 - e_3)}, k\}}, \qquad k^2 = \frac{e_2 - e_3}{e_1 - e_3}$$

a transformation $\omega = \wp(z)$ can be expressed in Schwarz–Christoffel form by the above integral, or in terms of the Jacobian E.F. sn $u$.

If we write $w = \wp\{z, g_2, g_3\}$, here is one example of the transformation $w = \wp(z)$ with $g_2 = 4$, $g_3 = 0$, $e_1 = -e_3 = 1$, $e_2 = 0$. The square with vertices $z = 0$, $\omega_1$, $(1+i)\omega_1$, $i\omega_1$ is mapped on the lower half of the $w$-plane, where

$$\omega_1 = \int_0^1 \frac{dt}{\sqrt{(1-t^4)}}, \qquad \omega_3 = i\omega_1.$$

The transformation is shown in the figure, where corresponding points and regions are marked by the same symbols. The details are left to the reader.

† See § 2.12.

For further examples of transformations involving E.F. see Kober, *Dictionary of Conformal Representations*.

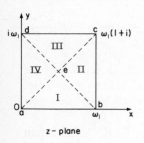
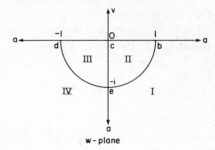

Fig. 14.

### 3.7 Schwarz's Lemma

*If $f(z)$ is regular within $|z| < 1$ and $f(0) = 0$, then, if within $|z| < 1$ $|f(z)| \leqslant 1$, we have $|f(z)| \leqslant |z|$ for $|z| < 1$. Equality can only hold if $f(z) = kz$ and $|k| = 1$.*

Since $f(0) = 0$ the function $f(z)/z$ is regular at $z = 0$ and so throughout the unit circle. If $0 < r < 1$ it follows from $|f(z)| \leqslant 1$ and the maximum-modulus principle† that,

$$\left|\frac{f(z)}{z}\right| \leqslant \frac{1}{r}, \quad |z| < r.$$

Since $r$ can be as near as we please to 1, we thus have

$$\left|\frac{f(z)}{z}\right| \leqslant 1 \quad \text{for } |z| < 1, \tag{1}$$

which proves the theorem apart from the equality case.

If for a point $\zeta$ in the unit circle $|f(z)| = |z|$ then the left-hand side of (1) takes the value 1 at $z = \zeta$. By the maximum-modulus principle it must therefore reduce to a constant $k$ where $|k| = 1$. Hence $f(z) = kz$ in this case and $|k| = 1$.

COROLLARY. *Since*

$$f(z) = f'(0)z + f''(0)\frac{z^2}{2!} + \dots$$

*it follows from (1) that $|f'(0)| \leqslant 1$, the equality holding only if $f(z) = kz, |k| = 1$.*

† See *P.C.V.*, § 42.

### 3.8 Extension of Schwarz's Lemma

If a regular function $f(z)$ satisfies $|f(z)| \leqslant M$ in any domain the function is *bounded*. Without loss of generality we can assume that $M = 1$, for if $M \neq 1$ we have only to divide $f(z)$ by $M$ to get a function of this type. We now prove that *Schwarz's lemma holds for functions which, although bounded in $|z| < 1$, do not vanish for $z = 0$.*

By *P.C.V.*, II, p. 52

$$w = e^{i\theta}\left(\frac{z-a}{1-\bar{a}z}\right), \quad 0 \leqslant \theta < 2\pi, \quad |a| < 1,$$

maps the unit circle on to itself.

Since $|f(z)| \leqslant 1$ for $|z| < 1$ the points $w_1 = f(z)$ will be within or on the circle $|w_1| = 1$. Hence

$$w = g(z) = \frac{f(z)-a}{1-\bar{a}f(z)}, \quad |a| < 1,$$

will satisfy $|w| \leqslant 1$. Hence $g(z)$ is regular and bounded in $|z| < 1$. Since $|f(0)| < 1$ we may take $a = f(0)$. We thus get the bounded function

$$g(z) = \frac{f(z)-f(0)}{1-\bar{f}(0)f(z)}$$

for which $g(0) = 0$. Hence we may apply Schwarz's lemma to $g(z)$, getting

$$|g(z)| \leqslant |z|. \tag{1}$$

Solving for $f(z)$ we have

$$f(z) = \frac{f(0)+g(z)}{1+\bar{f}(0)g(z)}. \tag{2}$$

(1) shows that if $|z| < r$ the values of $g(z)$ are within a circle of radius $r$ about the origin. Since, by (2), $f(z)$ is obtained from $g(z)$ by the Möbius transformation

$$w_1 = \frac{f(0)+w}{1+\bar{f}(0)w}, \tag{3}$$

the values of $f(z)$ must be contained in the interior of the circle $C$

on to which $|w| = r$ is mapped by (3). We have thus proved the extension of Schwarz's lemma to bounded functions $f(z)$ for which $f(0) \neq 0$.

It is easy to verify that if $|\alpha| < 1$, $|\beta| < 1$

$$\frac{|\alpha|-|\beta|}{1-|\alpha\beta|} \leqslant \frac{|\alpha+\beta|}{|1+\bar{\alpha}\beta|} \leqslant \frac{|\alpha|+|\beta|}{1+|\alpha\beta|}. \tag{4}$$

If $|w| < |f(0)|$ the circle $C$ does not contain the origin; hence the distance from the origin of any point within $C$ is larger than the distance from the origin of the point of $C$ which is nearest to the origin. From (2) and (4)

$$\frac{|f(0)|-|z|}{1-|f(0)||z|} \leqslant |f(z)| \leqslant \frac{|f(0)|+|z|}{1+|f(0)||z|}. \tag{5}$$

The left-hand side of (5) has been proved for $|z| < |f(0)|$; it is trivial for $|f(0)| \leqslant |z| < 1$.

### 3.9 An Estimate of the Derivative of a Bounded Function

If $f(z)$ is bounded in $|z| < 1$ this is also true of

$$g(z) = \frac{f(z)-f(z_0)}{1-\bar{f}(z_0)f(z)}, \quad |z_0| < 1,$$

and $g(z_0) = 0$. The function

$$\phi(z) = \frac{g(z)}{\dfrac{z-z_0}{1-\bar{z}_0z}} = \frac{f(z)-f(z_0)}{z-z_0} \cdot \frac{1-\bar{z}_0z}{1-\bar{f}(z_0)f(z)}$$

is thus regular at $z = z_0$ and also at all other points of $|z| < 1$. Further $\phi(z)$ is bounded in $|z| < 1$. Now $\varlimsup_{|z|\to 1} |g(z)| \leqslant 1$ and

$$\left|\frac{z-z_0}{1-\bar{z}_0z}\right| = 1$$

for $|z| = 1$, so by the maximum principle $|\phi(z)| \leqslant 1$ throughout $|z| < 1$. Now put $z = z_0$ and it follows from (1) that

$$|f'(z_0)|\left(\frac{1-|z_0|^2}{1-|f(z_0)|^2}\right) \leqslant 1,$$

or

$$|f'(z)| \leqslant \frac{1-|f(z)|^2}{1-|z|^2}.$$

### 3.10  Functions with a Positive Real Part

Suppose that $f(z)$ satisfies $\mathscr{R}f(z) \geqslant 0$ in $|z| < 1$. By the Möbius transformation

$$\zeta = \frac{w-1}{w+1}$$

the half-plane $\mathscr{R}w > 0$ is mapped on the unit circle $|\zeta| < 1$, the points $w = 0$, i, $\infty \sim \zeta = -1$, i, 1 respectively and $\zeta = 0$ when $w = 1$.

Hence if $\mathscr{R}f(z) \geqslant 0$,

$$g(z) = \frac{f(z)-1}{f(z)+1}$$

satisfies $|g(z)| \leqslant 1$. So any function $f(z)$ with positive real part can be written as

$$f(z) = \frac{1+g(z)}{1-g(z)}, \quad \text{where } |g(z)| \leqslant 1. \tag{1}$$

If now $f(0) = 1$ then $g(0) = 0$. We now use the inequality that when $|\alpha| < 1$

$$\left| \frac{1+\alpha}{1-\alpha} \right| \leqslant \frac{1+|\alpha|}{1-|\alpha|},$$

and it follows from (1), using Schwarz's lemma, that

$$|f(z)| \leqslant \frac{1+|z|}{1-|z|}. \tag{2}$$

There is no loss of generality by taking $f(0) = 1$, for if

$$f(0) = a+ib \quad (a > 0)$$

then

$$F(z) = \frac{1}{a}\{f(z)-ib\}$$

satisfies $\mathscr{R}F(z) \geqslant 0$, $F(0) = 1$, and (1) applies to $F(z)$.

A lower bound for $|f(z)|$ is obtained by noticing that $\{f(z)\}^{-1}$ also has a positive real part. For,

$$\mathscr{R}\left\{\frac{1}{f(z)}\right\} = \mathscr{R}\left\{\frac{\bar{f}(z)}{|f(z)|^2}\right\} = \mathscr{R}\left\{\frac{f(z)}{|f(z)|^2}\right\} \geqslant 0.$$

It follows from $\mathscr{R}f(z) \geqslant 0$ that $f(z) \neq 0$ for $|z| < 1$. Thus from (2) we get

$$\frac{1}{|f(z)|} \leqslant \frac{1+|z|}{1-|z|},$$

or

$$\frac{1-|z|}{1+|z|} \leqslant |f(z)| \leqslant \frac{1+|z|}{1-|z|}.$$

### 3.11 Schwarz's Symmetry Principle

*If a regular function $w = w(z)$ be defined in a region $D$ whose boundary is a portion $AB$ of the real axis and a curve $C$ in the upper half-plane, then if $w$ is continuous within and on $C$ and takes real values on $AB$, $w$ can be continued across the real axis.*

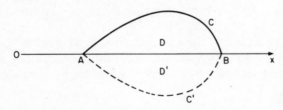

Fig. 15.

Let $C'$ be the image of $C$ in $Ox$. Consider

$$\frac{1}{2\pi i}\int \frac{w\,dz}{z-z_0} \quad \text{and} \quad \frac{1}{2\pi i}\int \frac{\bar{w}\,d\bar{z}}{\bar{z}-z_0} \tag{1}$$

the first round the boundary of $D$, the second round the boundary of $D'$. The value of the first integral is

$$\frac{1}{2\pi i}\int_C \frac{w\,dz}{z-z_0} + \frac{1}{2\pi i}\int_{AB} \frac{w(x)\,dx}{x-z_0},$$

and of the second

$$\frac{1}{2\pi i}\int_{C'} \frac{\overline{w}\,d\overline{z}}{\overline{z}-z_0}+\frac{1}{2\pi i}\int_{BA} \frac{\overline{w}(x)\,dx}{x-z_0}.$$

Since $\overline{w}(x) = w(x)$ the two integrals along $AB$ cancel in the sum of the two. Thus the sum of the two integrals in (1) is

$$\frac{1}{2\pi i}\int_{C+C'} \frac{\phi\,dz}{z-z_0}, \tag{2}$$

where $\phi = w(z)$ in the upper half-plane and $\overline{w}(z)$ in the lower half. For all points $z_0$ in the whole region $D+D'$, (2) represents a one-valued, continuous function of $z_0$; its value is $w(z_0)$ in $D$ and $\overline{w}(z_0)$ in $D'$, so $\overline{w}$ is the continuation into the lower half-plane of the function defined by $w$ in the upper half-plane.

### 3.12

The above theorem is a special case of a more general result.

*If two functions $f(z)$, $g(z)$ are regular in regions $D$ and $\Delta$ separated by a contour $C$ and if the functions are continuous on $C$ and $f(z) = g(z)$ along $C$, then the two functions are analytic continuations of each other.*

Let $AB$ be an arc of the curve $C$ dividing $D$ from $\Delta$. Let $APB$ be an arc in $D$ and $AQB$ an arc in $\Delta$ forming a contour $APBQA$ enclosing the arc $AB$. For a point $\zeta$ inside the contour $APBA$ and in $D$,

$$f(\zeta) = \frac{1}{2\pi i}\left[\int_{APB} \frac{f(z)\,dz}{z-\zeta}+\int_{BA} \frac{f(z)\,dz}{z-\zeta}\right],$$

$$0 = \frac{1}{2\pi i}\left[\int_{BQA} \frac{g(z)\,dz}{z-\zeta}+\int_{AB} \frac{g(z)\,dz}{z-\zeta}\right].$$

Hence by addition,

$$f(\zeta) = \frac{1}{2\pi i}\left[\int_{APB} \frac{f(z)\,dz}{z-\zeta}+\int_{BQA} \frac{g(z)\,dz}{z-\zeta}\right]. \tag{1}$$

We get the same expression for $g(\zeta)$ if $\zeta$ is a point in $\Delta$. The function $F(\zeta)$ represented by the right-hand side of (1) is a regular function in the domain $D+\Delta$ and is equal to $f(\zeta)$ in $D$ and to $g(\zeta)$ in $\Delta$. Hence $g(z)$ is the analytic continuation of $f(z)$ across the arc $AB$.

## Examples 3

**1.** Express the transformation,

$$w = \frac{z^2 - 6z + 10}{2z - 6},$$

in the form

$$\frac{w - \alpha}{w - \beta} = \left(\frac{z - c}{z - b}\right)^2$$

and find the finite regions of the $z$-plane which are mapped on the region $|w| < 1$, $\frac{1}{2}\pi < \arg w < \pi$.

**2.** Find the domain of the $w$-plane which represents the semicircle $|z| < 1, \mathscr{I}z > 0$. conformally by,

$$w = \left(\frac{2z - 1}{z - 2}\right)^2.$$

**3.** If

$$w = \frac{3z^2 - 8z + 12}{-2z^2 + 12z - 8}$$

show that $w = \pm 1$ correspond to pairs of equal values of $z$.

Find to what region of the $z$-plane the outside of the circle $4|w-1| = 5|w+1|$ corresponds. Illustrate in a diagram the regions of the $z$-plane which correspond to $|w| \leqslant 1, \mathscr{I}w \geqslant 0$.

**4.** Show that

$$w = k\left(\frac{z + c}{z - c}\right)^{\pi/\alpha}$$

maps a circular crescent with vertices $z = \pm c$ and angle $\alpha$ on a half-plane. (See P.C.V., III p. 68.)

Sketch the aerofoil boundary in the $w$-plane which corresponds (i) to a circle $C$ through $z = \pm c$, (ii) to a circle touching $C$ at $z = -c$ and enclosing $z = c$, by the transformation

$$\frac{w + c}{w - c} = \left(\frac{z + c}{z - c}\right)^n,$$

$c > 0, 0 < n < 2$.

**5.** Show that

$$w = \int_0^z \frac{dt}{\sqrt{\{t(1 - t^2)\}}}$$

maps the upper half of the $z$-plane on to the interior of a square of side $\Gamma^2(\frac{1}{4})/2\sqrt{(2\pi)}$, and that

$$w = \int_0^z \frac{dt}{\sqrt{\{1-t^4\}}}$$

maps $|z| < 1$ on to the interior of a square of diagona· equal to the side of the above square.

**6.** Show that the region, in the positive quadrant of the $w$-plane, bounded by the lines $u = 0, v = 0, u = 1(v > 1), v = 1(u > 1)$ is mapped on the upper half $z$-plane by

$$\pi w = \cosh^{-1}z - \sin^{-1}(1/z) + \frac{\pi}{2}.$$

**7.** Show that if we map the upper half $z$-plane on the interior of a triangle of angles $\pi\alpha, \pi\beta, \pi\gamma$ so that the vertices correspond to the points $z = 0, z = 1, z = \infty$, then if $a, b, c$ are the lengths of the sides of the triangle opposite the angles $\pi\alpha, \pi\beta, \pi\gamma$, $a = P \sin \pi\alpha$, $b = P \sin \pi\beta$, $c = P \sin \pi\gamma$ where $\pi P = \Gamma(\alpha)\Gamma(\beta)\Gamma(\gamma)$.

**8.** Show that by

$$w = \int_1^z \frac{\sqrt{(1+z^4)}}{z^2} dz$$

the area outside a square in the $w$-plane $\sim$ the interior of the unit circle in the $z$-plane and $z = 0 \sim w = \text{ }$

**9.** If $z = \text{sn}(w, k)$, show that when $k = 1/\sqrt{2}$, $K = K' = 1\cdot8541$. Show that $z = \text{sn}(w, 1/\sqrt{2})$ maps the square with vertices $0, K, iK, K+iK$ in the $w$-plane on the positive quadrant of the $z$-plane. Show that the diagonals $u = v, u+v = 1$ of this square $\sim$ portions of the lemniscate $|z-1||z+1| = 1$ and of the hyperbola $x^2 - y^2 = 1$. Indicate in a figure the regions of the $z$-plane which correspond to each of the four regions into which the diagonals divide the square in the $w$-plane.

**10.** Show that if $z = \text{sn}^2(\frac{1}{2}w, k)$ the curves $u = $ constant, $v = $ constant are confocal Cartesian ovals whose equations are,

$$\rho - r \, \text{dn}(u, k) = \text{cn}(u, k), \quad \rho + r \, \text{dn}(iv, k') = \text{cn}(iv, k'),$$

where $r$ and $\rho$ are the distances from the foci $z = 0$ and $z = 1$.

**11.** If $0 < k < 1$, show that as $z$ describes the sides of the rectangle with vertices $0, K, K+iK', iK'$, $\text{sn } z$ increases from 0 to $\infty$ along the first three sides and $i \, \text{sn } z$ increases from $-\infty$ to 0 along the fourth, $\text{sn}^2 z$ being real on the sides of the rectangle. Give the corresponding results for $\text{cn } z$.

Hence, or otherwise, show that as $z$ describes this rectangle, $w = \text{sn } z/(1 + \text{cn } z)$ describes a quadrant of the unit circle.

**12.** If $f(z)$ is bounded in $|z| < 1$, $f(0) = 0$ and $|f'(0)| = k$ show that $z^{-1}f(z)$ is bounded and hence that if $0 \leqslant \theta < 2\pi$

$$\rho(k-\rho) \leqslant (1-k\rho)|f(\rho e^{i\theta})|.$$

[Use § 3.8, eq. (5).]

**13.** Prove that if $f(z)$ is regular for $|z| \leqslant r$, $\mathscr{R}f(z) \leqslant 1(|z| = r)$ and $f(0) = \alpha + i\beta$, then

$$|f(z) - f(0)| \leqslant \frac{2(1-\alpha)|z|}{r - |z|}.$$

**14.** If $f(z)$ is regular and $|f(z)| \leq 1$ when $|z| < 1$ and $f(a) = 0$ where $0 < a < 1$, show by means of the transformation

$$w = \frac{z-a}{1-az}$$

that

$$|f(z)| \leq \frac{|z|+a}{1-a|z|}$$

whenever $|z| < 1$.

**15.** If $f(z)$ is regular for $|z| < 1$ and not a constant, and if $|f(z)| < 1$ for $|z| < 1$, show by considering the function

$$\phi(z) = \frac{f(z)-f(0)}{1-\bar{f}(0)f(z)},$$

and using Cauchy's integral for $\phi'(0)$, that

$$|f'(0)| \leq 1-|f(0)|^2.$$

**16.** The function $f(z)$ is regular in $|z| < R$, its real part is never negative and $f(0) = 1$. If $u+iv = f(z)$ show that, if $|z| < R$,

$$|v| \leq \frac{2R|z|}{R^2-|z|^2}.$$

(See § 3.10.)

## CHAPTER 4

# SCHLICHT FUNCTIONS

## 4.1

We begin with a fundamental theorem on conformal transformation.

THEOREM A. *Suppose that $f(z)$ is regular at $z = a$ and that $f(a) = b$. Then $f$ takes, near $a$, any value near enough to $b$.*

Let us make this more precise as follows. If $z = a$ is a zero of $f(z) - b$ of order $n$, then for every sufficiently small $s$ there exists an $r$, which tends to zero with $s$, such that for every $c$ satisfying $|c - b| \leqslant s$ there are exactly $n$ solutions of $f(z) = c$ in $|z - a| < r$. Further, if $\rho$ is sufficiently small, $f$ takes no value more than $n$ times in $|z - a| < \rho$.

Suppose that $a = 0$ and that for small $z$

$$f(z) - b = a_n z^n + a_{n+1} z^{n+1} + \dots \quad (n > 0, \, a_n \neq 0).$$

For small $r$,

$$|a_{n+1} z^{n+1} + \dots | < \tfrac{1}{4}|a_n| r^n \quad (|z| = r).$$

If now $s = \tfrac{1}{4}|a_n| r^n$ and $|c - b| < s$ then $f(z) - c = F + \phi$, where

$$F = a_n z^n \text{ and } \phi = (b - c) + (a_{n+1} z^{n+1} + \dots)$$

and on

$$|z| = r, \quad |\phi| < \tfrac{1}{2}|a_n| r^n, \quad |\phi/F| < \tfrac{1}{2} < 1.$$

Round $|z| = r$ we have

$$\Delta \arg(f - c) = \Delta \arg F + \Delta \arg(1 + \phi/F) = 2n\pi + 0.$$

Hence $f(z) - c$ has $n$ zeros in $|z| < r$.

If $s, r$ have the above properties then any positive real number $\rho \leqslant r$, such that $|f(z) - b| \leqslant s$ for all $z$ satisfying $|z - a| \leqslant \rho$, will have the desired property.

## 4.2 Definition

A regular function $f(z)$ is called schlicht[†] in $D$ if $f(z_1) \neq f(z_2)$ for every pair of distinct points $z_1, z_2$ of $D$. Such functions will be called, for brevity, $S$ functions.

If $w = f(z)$ is schlicht, then it represents the region $D$ of the $z$-plane on a region $\Delta$ of the $w$-plane in such a way that there is a one-one correspondence between the points of $D$ and $\Delta$. We now prove some elementary properties of schlicht functions.

(1) *If $f(z)$ is schlicht in $D$ then $f'(z) \neq 0$ in $D$.* Suppose that $f'(z_0) = 0$; then $f(z) - f(z_0)$ has a zero of order $n \geqslant 2$ at $z_0$. We can find a circle $|z - z_0| = k$ on which $f(z) - f(z_0)$ does not vanish and inside which $f'(z)$ has no zeros except $z_0$. Let $m$ be the lower bound of $|f(z) - f(z_0)|$ on this circle. Then by Rouché's theorem,[‡] if $0 < |a| < m$, $f(z) - f(z_0) - a$ has $n \, (> 2)$ zeros in the circle, which is a contradiction of the fact that $f(z)$ does not take any value more than once. Hence $f'(z_0) \neq 0$ in $D$.

We have given this independent proof, but the result is also a deduction from Theorem A in the case $n = 1$.

(2) *A schlicht function of a schlicht function is schlicht.* If $f(z)$ is schlicht in $D$ and $F(w)$ in $\Delta$ then $F\{f(z)\}$ is schlicht in $D$, for $F\{f(z_1)\} = F\{f(z_2)\}$ implies $f(z_1) = f(z_2)$ since $F$ is schlicht and this implies that $z_1 = z_2$ since $f$ is schlicht.

(3) *The inverse function of $w = f(z)$ is schlicht if $f(z)$ is.* Let the inverse function be $z = \phi(w)$. Then $\phi(w)$ is one-valued and it does not take any value more than once, since $f(z)$ is one-valued. Also it is regular, for if $w_1 = f(z_1)$ then

$$\frac{w - w_1}{z - z_1} \to f'(z_1) \quad \text{as} \quad z \to z_1.$$

Hence, since $f'(z_1) \neq 0$,

$$\frac{z - z_1}{w - w_1} \to \frac{1}{f'(z_1)},$$

as $w \to w_1$.

(4) *Let $f_1(z), f_2(z), \ldots$ be a sequence of functions which are regular in $D$ and converge to a function $f(z)$ regular in $D$. If $c$ is a point in $D$ and $f(c) = 0$, then there must be a zero of $f_n(z)$ within the circle $|z - c| < \varepsilon$ for all $n$ large enough.*

[†] Also called *simple*, *univalent* or *biuniform*.
[‡] See *P.C.V.*, p. 108.

Take $\varepsilon$ small enough for all the points of $|z-c| = \varepsilon$ to be within $D$ and so that $f(z)$ does not vanish in $|z-c| \leqslant \varepsilon$ except at $c$. Since $f(z)$ is continuous on the circle $C$, $|z-c| = \varepsilon$, there is a number $m$ such that $|f(z)| > m$ on this circle. The sequence $\{f_n(z)\}$ converges uniformly on $C$ and so $|f(z)-f_n(z)| < m$ for $|z-c| = \varepsilon$ if $n$ is taken large enough. Hence on $C$

$$|f(z)-f_n(z)| < m < |f(z)|.$$

By Rouché's theorem,

$$f_n(z) = f(z) + \{f_n(z)-f(z)\}$$

has the same number of zeros inside $C$ as $f(z)$. But $f(z)$ has one zero $z = c$ within $C$. Hence the same is true of $f_n(z)$.

COROLLARY. *If the functions $f_1(z), f_2(z), \ldots$ are schlicht in $D$ then so is $f(z)$.*

Suppose that for two points $z_1, z_2$ in $D$, $f(z_1) = f(z_2)$. Consider the sequence of functions $g_n(z) = f_n(z)-f_n(z_1)$. Since $f_n(z)$ is schlicht, $g_n(z) \neq 0$ except at $z = z_1$. The limit function $g(z) = f(z)-f(z_1)$ vanishes at $z = z_2$, so by the theorem $g_n(z)$ must vanish within an arbitrarily small neighbourhood of $z_2$ if $n$ is large enough. Since $g_n(z)$ does not vanish in $D$ except at $z_1$ this is impossible. The contradiction establishes that $f(z)$ is schlicht in $D$.

THEOREM B. *Let a domain $D$ in the $z$-plane be enclosed by a contour $C$ and let $f(z)$ be regular in $D$ and continuous on $C$. Suppose that as $z$ describes $C$ in the positive sense, $w = f(z)$ describes a closed contour $\Gamma$ once. Then $\Gamma$ is described in the positive sense and $w = f(z)$ maps $D$ conformally on $\Delta$, the interior of $\Gamma$.*

Suppose $z_0$ is a point of $D$ and let $p = f(z_0)$, then

$$\Delta_C \arg\{f(z)-f(z_0)\} = \Delta_\Gamma \arg\{w-f(z_0)\}. \tag{1}$$

The left-hand side is $2\pi$ times the number of roots of $f(z) = f(z_0)$ in $D$, so it is at least $2\pi$. Hence $p$ cannot be outside $\Delta$ or the right-hand side would be zero. If $p$ were a point on $\Gamma$, $f(z)$ would take, near $z_0$, all values near $p$, so would take values that are outside $\Gamma$, which we have seen it cannot do. Hence $p$ is an interior point of $\Delta$, eqn. (1) holds, and the right-hand side is $\pm 2\pi$ according as $\Gamma$ is described in the positive or negative sense; but the left-hand side is not less than $2\pi$. Hence $\Gamma$ is described in the positive sense.

Finally, if $w_0$ belongs to $\Delta$, and so $f(z) \neq w_0$ for $z$ on $C$,

$$\Delta_C \arg\{f(z) - w_0\} = \Delta_\Gamma \arg(w - w_0) = 2\pi;$$

so there is one and only one $z$ in $D$ giving $f(z) = w_0$.

It follows that $f(z)$ is schlicht and its values fill the domain $\Delta$.

Theorem B is important in applications in which we are given $D$ and $\Delta$ and have to find the function $w = f(z)$ which effects the required mapping. We see that it is enough to find a function $f(z)$ which is regular and behaves correctly on the boundary $C$.

In Theorem B both the domains considered are bounded. If we suppose that $D$ is to be mapped onto a half-plane, the theorem corresponding to B requires an additional restriction. We state it as Theorem B′.

THEOREM B′. *Let $C$ be a closed contour starting from and ending at $z = a$, let $f(z)$ be regular inside $C$, continuous on $C$, except at $a$, while $f(z) \to \infty$ uniformly as $z \to a$ in $D$. Suppose that as $z$ describes $C$, $w = f(z)$ describes the real axis from $-\infty$ to $\infty$, then $w = f(z)$ maps $D$ conformally on $\mathscr{P}$, the upper half of the $w$-plane, provided that there shall exist a $w_0$, not real, such that $f(z) \neq w_0$ in $D$.*

If $\zeta = (w - w_0)^{-1}$, it can be seen that $\zeta$ describes the circle $\zeta^2 + \eta^2 - \eta/v_0 = 0$ as $w$ goes from $-\infty$ to $\infty$. Let this circle be $\Gamma$, of interior $\Delta$, then this transformation represents $\Delta$ on that half $w$-plane in which $w_0$ does not lie, and $\Gamma$ is described in the positive or negative sense according to $w_0$ does not or does lie in $\mathscr{P}$. Now consider $\zeta = \phi(z) = 1/\{f(z) - w_0\}$. It is regular in $D$, continuous on $C$, including $z = a$, and as $z$ describes $C$, $f(z)$ describes $-\infty$ to $\infty$ and $\zeta$ describes $\Gamma$ once. Hence $\zeta = \phi(z)$ represents $D$ on $\Delta$. Also $\Gamma$ is described in the positive sense so $w_0$ is not in $\mathscr{P}$. Combining the transformations $w = f(z)$ maps $D$ on $\mathscr{P}$.

To show that this theorem is untrue without the last proviso in the enunciation, consider $w = f(z) = i(1+z)/(1-z)$. This maps $|z| < 1$ on $\mathscr{P}$ and as $z$ describes $|z| = 1$, starting with $z = 1$, $f(z)$ increases steadily from $-\infty$ to $\infty$. Now consider $t = w^3$. $t$ increases steadily from $-\infty$ to $\infty$ as $|z| = 1$ is described and $t \to \infty$ as $z \to 1$. But if $\mathscr{I}w_0 > 0$, two of the cube roots of $w_0$ lie in $\mathscr{P}$ and are values of $f(z)$, so that the value $w_0$ is taken twice by $t$. If $\mathscr{I}w_0 < 0$ only one cube root lies in $\mathscr{P}$ and $t$ takes the value $w_0$ only once.

It is therefore clear that some extra condition is needed, which is equivalent to $\mathscr{I} w_0 < 0$, in order to make Theorem B' true.†

## 4.3 Some Distortion Theorems

There has been an extensive literature on schlicht functions during recent years, and we shall only consider some of the simplest properties of such functions here. In the theorems to be considered we shall, in general, confine our attention to the unit circle. Since by Riemann's theorem‡ any simply-connected domain can be mapped on to the unit circle, any schlicht function in $D$ can be associated with a schlicht function in the unit circle; and the properties of the latter can then be translated into properties of the function in $D$ whenever the function mapping $D$ on to the unit circle is known.

A function which is regular and schlicht in the unit circle $(U)$ may be arranged so as to satisfy $f(0) = 0$, $f'(0) = 1$. For, if $f(z)$ is schlicht, so is the function

$$F(z) = \frac{f(z) - f(0)}{f'(0)},$$

and division by $f'(0)$ is always possible since the derivative of a schlicht function does not vanish. The class of S functions, normalized by the conditions $f(0) = 0$, $f'(0) = 1$, will be denoted by NS. When the domain in question is the unit circle we may write NS in $U$.

There exist S functions which are not regular in $U$. The function

$$\phi(z) = \frac{af(z) + b}{cf(z) + d},$$

$ad - bc \neq 0$, where $f(z)$ is S, is clearly S in $|z| < 1$, but it will have a simple pole if $-d/c$ is one of values taken by $f(z)$ in $U$. But an S function can have no other singularities, otherwise the value $\infty$ would be taken more than once. We now arrange that the class of S functions with one simple pole in $U$ shall have that pole at the origin and the residue at that pole shall be unity.

---

† For further details see Littlewood, *Theory of Functions* (1944), § 11.52.

‡ This is quoted, but not proved, in *P.C.V.*, §19. For a proof, see Dienes, *The Taylor Series:* p. 276 *et al.*

For, if $f(z)$ has its pole at $z = a$, where $|a| < 1$, we consider instead the function

$$g(z) = f\left(\frac{z+a}{1+\bar{a}z}\right).$$

Since $w = (z+a)(1+\bar{a}z)^{-1}$ maps the unit circle onto itself,† $g(z)$ is also S in $U$ and the pole of $g(z)$ is at $z = 0$. By multiplying by a suitable constant the residue at the pole can be made unity. The class of S functions in $U$ with Laurent expansion

$$f(z) = \tfrac{1}{z} + b_0 + b_1 z + b_2 z^2 + \ldots \tag{1}$$

we shall denote by PS.

THEOREM I. *The coefficients of a PS function satisfy*

$$\sum_{n=1}^{\infty} n|b_n|^2 \leqslant 1. \tag{2}$$

Let $D$ be the domain upon which $U$ is mapped by $w = f(z)$, when $f(z)$ is given by (1), let $E$ be the complement of $D$, and $C$ their common boundary. $C$ will be traversed in the negative sense with respect to $D$ if it is traversed in the positive sense with respect to $E$. Take $R, \phi$ as polar coordinates in the $w$-plane and $r, \theta$ as polar coordinates of the circle $|z| = r$ whose image is the curve $C$, then the area of $E$ will be

$$A = \frac{1}{2}\int_C R^2 \, d\phi = -\frac{1}{2}\int_0^{2\pi} R^2 \frac{\partial \phi}{\partial \theta} \, d\theta;$$

the negative sign indicates that the positive sense with respect to $E$ is the negative sense with respect to $D$ and so with respect to $|z| = r$. Since, by the Cauchy–Riemann equations,

$$\frac{\partial \phi}{\partial \theta} = \frac{r}{R}\frac{\partial R}{\partial r},$$

$$A = -\frac{r}{2}\int_0^{2\pi} R\frac{\partial R}{\partial r} \, d\theta = -\frac{r}{4}\frac{\partial}{\partial r}\left\{\int_0^{2\pi} R^2 \, d\theta\right\}$$

$$= -\frac{r}{4}\frac{\partial}{\partial r}\left\{\int_0^{2\pi} |f(re^{i\theta})|^2 \, d\theta\right\}.$$

† See *P.C.V.*, p. 52.

6

But

$$\int_0^{2\pi} |f(re^{i\theta})|^2 \, d\theta = \int_0^{2\pi} f(re^{i\theta})\bar{f}(re^{i\theta}) \, d\theta$$

$$= \int_0^{2\pi} \left\{ \frac{1}{re^{i\theta}} + \sum_0^\infty b_n r^n e^{ni\theta} \right\} \left\{ \frac{1}{r\,e^{-i\theta}} + \sum_0^\infty \bar{b}_n r^n e^{-ni\theta} \right\} d\theta$$

$$= 2\pi \left\{ \frac{1}{r^2} + \sum_0^\infty |b_n|^2 r^{2n} \right\},$$

all other terms being zero; the term-by-term integration is justified by uniform convergence. Hence

$$A = -\frac{\pi r}{2} \frac{\partial}{\partial r} \left\{ \frac{1}{r^2} + \sum |b_n|^2 r^{2n} \right\}$$

or

$$\frac{A}{\pi} = \frac{1}{r^2} - \sum n|b_n|^2 r^{2n}.$$

Since $A$ must be $\geqslant 0$, we have

$$\sum n|b_n|^2 r^{2n} \leqslant \frac{1}{r^2}.$$

Since this inequality holds for all values of $r$ between 0 and 1 it is true for $r \to 1$, which proves the theorem.

COROLLARY. *There exists a function PS for which $|b_1| = 1$.*

It follows from (2) that $|b_1| \leqslant |$ and $|b_1| = 1$ only if $b_2 = b_3 = \ldots = 0$.

Then (1) reduces to

$$f_0(z) = \frac{1}{z} + b_0 + b_1 z,$$

where $|b_1| = 1$.

We can put $b_0 = 0$ since this is only equivalent to a parallel shift of the map of $U$. We write $b_1 = e^{2i\lambda}$, where $0 \leqslant \lambda < 2\pi$. Then

$$w = f_0(z) = \frac{1}{z} + z\,e^{2i\lambda}.$$

So $f_0(e^{i\theta}) = 2\,e^{i\lambda} \cos(\theta + \lambda)$. So, as $z$ describes $U$, $w$ traverses both sides of a linear segment of length 4 with mid-point the origin, inclined at $\lambda$ to the real axis. Hence $w = f_0(z)$ is S in $|z| < 1$, and maps $|z| < 1$ on the whole $w$-plane with a cut along the line described above. Hence equality in $|b_1| \leqslant 1$ can only hold for functions mapping $|z| < 1$ on the whole $w$-plane, cut as described above.

### 4.4

THEOREM II. *For functions NS defined in § 4.3 to be of the form*

$$f(z) = z + a_2 z^2 + a_3 z^3 + \ldots \tag{1}$$

*we now prove that* $|a_2| \leqslant 2$.

The reciprocal of $f(z)$ is a function PS, since

$$\frac{1}{f(z)} = \frac{1}{z(1 + a_2 z + a_3 z^2 + \ldots)}$$

$$= \frac{1}{z}\left\{1 - (a_2 z + a_3 z^2 + \ldots) + (a_2 z + a_3 z^2 + \ldots)^2 - \ldots\right\}$$

$$= \frac{1}{z} - a_2 + (a_2^2 - a_3)z + \ldots;$$

so we have, using $|b_1| \leqslant 1$,

$$|a_2^2 - a_3| \leqslant 1. \tag{2}$$

From this result we can get an inequality involving $a_2$ only, for

$$g(z) = \sqrt{f(z^2)} = z\sqrt{\{1 + a_2 z^2 + a_3 z^4 + \ldots\}} = z + \tfrac{1}{2} a_2 z^3 + \ldots \tag{3}$$

is regular, and S in $U$, if the same is true of (1).

For, from $g(z_1) = g(z_2)$, where $z_1 \neq z_2, |z_1| < 1, |z_2| < 1$, it would follow that

$$f(z_1^2) = f(z_2^2).$$

But, since $f(z)$ is S in $U$ and both $z_1$ and $z_2$ are points in $U$, this involves that $z_1^2 = z_2^2$. Since $z_1 \neq z_2$, we must have $z_1 = -z_2$. But we cannot have $g(z_1) = g(-z_1)$ for $z_1 \neq 0$, since by (3), $g(z)$ is an odd function. The second and third coefficients of the S function $g(z)$ are 0 and $\tfrac{1}{2} a_2$ respectively, so on using (2) we get $|a_2| \leqslant 2$.

THEOREM III. *The conformal map of $U$, given by the NS function $w = f(z)$, of Theorem II, contains all the points in $|w| < \tfrac{1}{4}$.*

Suppose that $w_0$ is a value not taken by $f(z)$ in $|z| < 1$. The function

$$\phi(z) = \frac{w_0 f(z)}{w_0 - f(z)} = z + \left(a_2 + \frac{1}{w_0}\right)z^2 + \ldots \tag{1}$$

is regular in $U$ and it is also S in $U$ since the linear transformation of an S function leads to an S function. By Theorem II, it follows that

$$\left| a_2 + \frac{1}{w_0} \right| \leqslant 2$$

or

$$\frac{1}{|w_0|} \leqslant 2 + |a_2| \leqslant 4,$$

the second inequality following by another application of Theorem II. Hence $|w_0| \geqslant \frac{1}{4}$. This shows that the map of $U$ by the NS function

$$w = f(z) = z + a_2 z^2 + a_3 z^3 + \ldots,$$

contains all the points of the circle $|w| < \frac{1}{4}$.

The conformal map of a domain $D$ onto a domain $\Delta$ can be regarded as a "distortion" of the shape of $D$ resulting in the shape of $\Delta$.

Theorem III is sometimes called a *distortion theorem*, for it limits the distortion of the boundary of $U$ in the conformal mapping by means of a function NS; this boundary cannot be distorted so far as to come within a distance from the origin less than $\frac{1}{4}$. We can extend the result of Theorem III by means of,

THEOREM IV. *If $\alpha$ and $\beta$ are two values not taken by a function NS in $U$ and if the straight line joining $\alpha$ and $\beta$ goes through the origin $O$, then the distance of either $\alpha$ or $\beta$ from $O$ exceeds $\frac{1}{2}$, or both distances are equal to $\frac{1}{2}$.*

Consider the function $\phi(z)$ defined in (1) of Theorem III. Since $\alpha$ and $\beta$ are two values not taken by the NS function $f(z)$ of equation (1) in Theorem II, then the function $\phi(z)$ is regular and S in $U$ and does not take there the value $\alpha\beta/(\alpha - \beta)$. By Theorem III the modulus of this number must not exceed $\frac{1}{4}$. Hence

$$\left| \frac{1}{\alpha} - \frac{1}{\beta} \right| \leqslant 4.$$

Suppose now that $O$ lies between $\alpha$ and $\beta$, then $\alpha = |\alpha|e^{i\theta}$, $\beta = -|\beta|e^{i\theta}$ so that

$$\frac{1}{|\alpha|} + \frac{1}{|\beta|} \leqslant 4.$$

Hence at least one of $|\alpha|$, $|\beta|$ must exceed $\frac{1}{2}$ unless $|\alpha| = |\beta| = \frac{1}{2}$. This proves the theorem.

By means of the function $z(1-z^2)^{-1}$ it can be shown that the constant $\frac{1}{2}$ is the largest possible. This is left as an exercise for the reader.

## 4.5 Koebe's Distortion Theorems

THEOREM V. *For functions NS in U, if r is a positive number less than unity, we have*

$$\frac{1-r}{(1+r)^3} \leqslant |f'(z)| \leqslant \frac{1+r}{(1-r)^3};$$

$$\frac{r}{(1+r)^2} \leqslant |f(z)| \leqslant \frac{r}{(1-r)^2}.$$

We have already seen that $f\{(z+a)/(1+\bar{a}z)\}$, where $|a| < 1$, is S in $U$ if the same is true of $f(z)$.

The function

$$g(z) = \frac{f\{(z+a)/(1+\bar{a}z)\} - f(a)}{f'(a)\{1 - |a|^2\}},$$

clearly satisfies $g(0) = 0$, $g'(0) = 1$ and so is a function NS.

The second coefficient in the Taylor expansion of $g(z)$ is

$$\frac{1}{2}\left\{\frac{f''(a)(1-|a|^2)}{f'(a)} - 2\bar{a}\right\},$$

and so, by Theorem II, its modulus cannot exceed 2. Hence

$$\left|\frac{f''(a)(1-|a|^2)}{f'(a)} - 2\bar{a}\right| \leqslant 4.$$

Replacing $a$ by $z$, we get

$$\left|\frac{zf''(z)}{f'(z)} - \frac{2|z|^2}{1-|z|^2}\right| \leqslant \frac{4|z|}{1-|z|^2}. \tag{1}$$

If now $|z| = r < 1$

$$\frac{2r^2 - 4r}{1 - r^2} \leqslant \mathscr{R}\left\{\frac{zf''(z)}{f'(z)}\right\} \leqslant \frac{4r + 2r^2}{1 - r^2}. \tag{2}$$

Since

$$\mathscr{R}\left\{\frac{zf''(z)}{f'(z)}\right\} = \mathscr{R}\left\{\frac{\partial \log f'(z)}{\partial \log z}\right\} = r\frac{\partial}{\partial r}\mathscr{R}[\log f'(z)] = r\frac{\partial}{\partial r}\log|f'(z)|,$$

(2) may be written

$$\frac{2r - 4}{1 - r^2} \leqslant \frac{\partial}{\partial r}\log|f'(z)| \leqslant \frac{4 + 2r}{1 - r^2};$$

on integrating these from 0 to $r$, using partial fractions, we get

$$\log(1 - r) - 3\log(1 + r) \leqslant \log|f'(z)| \leqslant \log(1 + r) - 3\log(1 - r)$$

or

$$\frac{1 - r}{(1 + r)^3} \leqslant |f'(z)| \leqslant \frac{1 + r}{(1 - r)^3}, \tag{3}$$

where $|z| = r < 1$.

For the second theorem, we integrate (3) along the straight line from 0 to $z$, then

$$|f(z)| = \left|\int_0^z f'(t)\,dt\right| \leqslant \int_0^r |f'(z)|\,dr \leqslant \int_0^r \frac{1 + r}{(1 - r)^3}\,dr = \frac{r}{(1 - r)^2}.$$

To get the lower bound for $|f(z)|$ we assume first that $|f(z)| < \frac{1}{4}$. By Theorem III the straight line $L_1$ connecting the origin to the point $f(z)$ will be entirely covered by the values of $f(z)$ in $U$. If $L$ is the arc in $U$ mapped by $w = f(z)$ onto $L_1$ we have $dw = f'(z)\,dz > 0$ on $L$. Hence

$$|f(z)| = \left|\int_L f'(z)\,dz\right| = \int_L |f'(z)|\,dr \geqslant \int_0^r \frac{1 - r}{(1 + r)^3}\,dr = \frac{r}{(1 + r)^2}.$$

But $r(1 + r)^{-2} < \frac{1}{4}$ for $0 \leqslant r < 1$, so this inequality is clearly true if $|f(z)| \geqslant \frac{1}{4}$; hence it holds in all cases.

We have therefore

$$\frac{r}{(1+r)^2} \leqslant |f(z)| \leqslant \frac{r}{(1-r)^2}$$

when $|z| = r < 1$. This proves the second theorem.

## 4.6 Bieberbach's Inequality

THEOREM VI. *For the function $w = f(z) = z + a_2 z^2 + a_3 z^3 + \ldots$, which is NS in $U$,*

$$|a_n| \leqslant 5 \cdot 1 \, n^2.$$

From Theorem V (2) we have $|f(z)| \leqslant r(1-r)^{-2}$ and so by Cauchy's result† we have for every $r < 1$,

$$|a_n| \leqslant \frac{1}{r^n} \frac{r}{(1-r)^2}.$$

We find the value, for fixed $n$, for which the right-hand side is a minimum is given by $r = (n-1)/(n+1)$, whence

$$|a_n| \leqslant \left(\frac{n+1}{n-1}\right)^{n-1} \frac{(n+1)^2}{4} = \tfrac{1}{4}(n^2-1)\left\{\left(1+\frac{2}{n-1}\right)^{(n-1)/2}\right\}^{(2n/n-1)}.$$

Hence

$$|a_n| < \frac{n^2}{4}\exp\left(\frac{2n}{n-1}\right) \leqslant \frac{n^2 e^3}{4} \qquad \text{for } n \geqslant 3.$$

Since $\tfrac{1}{4}e^3 < 5 \cdot 1$, and by Theorem II $|a_2| \leqslant 2$, the inequality is established.

## Examples 4

**1.** Show that the function $w = \phi(z) = z(1-z)^{-2}$ is schlicht in $|z| < 1$ and maps $|z| < 1$ on the whole $w$-plane cut along the negative axis from $-\tfrac{1}{4}$ to $-\infty$.
Show also that $|a_2| = 2$ only if $w = e^{-i\lambda}\phi(e^{i\lambda}z)$, $0 \leqslant \lambda < 2\pi$.
Prove that the function $w = \phi(z)$ does not take the value $w = -\tfrac{1}{4}$ in $|z| < 1$, so that the constant $\tfrac{1}{4}$ of Theorem III cannot be replaced by any larger number.
**2.** Show that the function $z(1-z)^{-3}$ is schlicht for $|z| < \tfrac{1}{3}$, but not in any circle of larger radius and centre at the origin.
Discuss similarly $(1-3z)/(1-z)^2$ in relation to $|z| < \tfrac{1}{3}$.
**3.** Prove that $f(z) = z + a_2 z^2 + a_3 z^3 + \ldots$ is schlicht for $|z| < 1$ if

$$\sum_{n=2}^{\infty} n|a_n| \leqslant 1.$$

† *P.C.V.*, p. 96, Corollary to Taylor's theorem.

**4.** By applying the second of the Theorems V to

$$g(z) = \frac{f\{(z+a)/(1+\bar{a}z)\} - f(a)}{f'(a)\{1 - |a|^2\}}$$

and putting $z = -a$ in the result, prove that an NS function $f(z)$ satisfies

$$\frac{1}{r}\left(\frac{1-r}{1+r}\right) \leqslant \left|\frac{f'(z)}{f(z)}\right| \leqslant \frac{1}{r}\left(\frac{1+r}{1-r}\right),$$

where $|z| = r < 1$.

**5.** Show that, if an NS function $f(z)$ satisfies $|f(z)| \leqslant M$ for $|z| < 1$, then the function

$$g(z) = f(z)\left\{1 + \frac{e^{i\theta}}{M}f(z)\right\}^{-2},$$

where $0 \leqslant \theta < 2\pi$, is NS in $|z| < 1$.

Hence deduce that, for $f(z)$,

$$|a_2| \leqslant 2(1 - M^{-1}).$$

**6.** Show that, for a function NS in $U$,

$$|\arg f'(z)| \leqslant 2\log\frac{1+r}{1-r},$$

where $r = |z|$.

(Use eqn. (1) in Theorem V.)

**7.** $w = f(z)$ is NS in $U$. If the map $G$ in the $w$-plane does not contain $w = \infty$ and $d$ is the shortest distance of the boundary of $G$ from $w = 0$, show that

$$d \geqslant \frac{1}{|a_2| + 2}$$

and that equality holds if $f(z) = z/\{1 + e^{i\lambda}z\}^2$ where $\lambda$ is real.

[Apply Theorem II to $f(z)/\{1 - h^{-1}f(z)\}$ where $h$ is a boundary point of $G$.]

**8.** Let $E$ denote the class of functions $f(z)$ which are regular and schlicht in $D$ and satisfy $|f(z)| \leqslant 1$ for all $z$ in $D$. If $\zeta$ is a point of $D$, show that there exists a function $f_1(z)$ of the class $E$ such that $|f'(\zeta)| \leqslant |f_1'(\zeta)|$, where $f(z)$ is any other function of the class $E$.

**9.** If $f(z)$ is NS in $U$, and the coefficients $a_n$ are real, prove that $|a_n| \leqslant n$.

**10.** If $f(z)$ is NS in $U$, and $f(z)$ is an odd function, so that

$$w = f(z) = z + a_3 z^3 + a_5 z^5 + \dots$$

show that $w = f(z)$ maps $U$ on to a domain covering the circle $|w| < \frac{1}{2}$ completely.

(Use the method of Theorem III, § 4.4.)

**11.** Find a schlicht transformation which maps $0 < \mathscr{I}z < 1$ onto $0 < \mathscr{I}w < 1$. $\mathscr{R}w > 0$. Discuss how the boundaries correspond under this transformation. (Liv.)†

**12.** Prove that

$$w = u + iv = \log\frac{1+z}{1-z}$$

† Questions marked (Liv.) are taken, with the Senate's permission, from degree papers of Liverpool University.

maps $|z| < 1$ on to the strip $|v| < \frac{1}{2}\pi$, the value of the logarithm being that which vanishes when $z = 0$. Show that under this mapping any line $v = $ const. is the image of an arc of a circle through $-1$ and $1$.

Find the points on $|z| = r(<1)$ whose images have least distance from the boundary of $|v| < \frac{1}{2}\pi$. Show that this minimum distance is $\frac{1}{2}\pi - 2\tan^{-1}r$. Find also the maximum value of $u$ on $|z| = r$. (Liv.)

CHAPTER 5

# THE MAXIMUM-MODULUS PRINCIPLE

## 5.1 The Maximum-Modulus Theorem

THEOREM A. *If* $|f(z)| \leqslant M$ *on* $C$, *then* $|f(z)| < M$ *at all points interior to the domain* $D$ *enclosed by* $C$ *unless* $f(z)$ *is a constant, in which case* $|f(z)| = M$ *everywhere.*

This theorem, which is very important in the applications of complex variable theory, was proved in *P.C.V.*, p. 110.

The theorem has only been proved for regular functions, but it is also true for functions which are not one-valued, provided that $|f(z)|$ is one-valued, for the proof holds for any branch of the function $f(z)$. For example, the theorem is true for $\sqrt{z}$ in a ring-shaped region about the origin.

We denote by $M(r)$ the maximum value of $|f(z)|$ on the circle $|z| = r$ and we define $A(r)$ and $B(r)$ as the maxima of the real and imaginary parts of $f(z)$. If we suppose that $f(z) = \Sigma a_n z^n$ is convergent in $|z| < R$, and $r < R$, then if $f(z) = u(r, \theta) + iv(r, \theta)$,

$$A(r) = \max u(r, \theta), \quad B(r) = \max v(r, \theta), \quad 0 \leqslant \theta < 2\pi.$$

THEOREM B. *The functions* $M(r)$, $A(r)$ *and* $B(r)$ *are steadily increasing functions of* $r$, *unless* $f(z)$ *is a constant.*

We prove this result for $M(r)$: the proofs for $A(r)$ and $B(r)$ are similar.

Along $|z| = r$, $|f(z)|$ is a continuous function of $\theta$. Hence there is a point $z_0$ of this circumference at which $|f(z)|$ assumes its maximum, i.e. $|f(z_0)| = M(r)$. Now if there were a circle $|z| = \rho > r$ in which $|f(z)| \leqslant M(r)$, $|f(z)|$ would have a maximum at the inner point $z_0$ and so, by the preceding theorem, $f(z)$ would be constant.

We can state the maximum-modulus theorem in the form "there can be no maximum-modulus inside $|z| = R$" because the form "$|f(z)|$ assumes its maximum at a boundary point" is less general; for $f(z)$ may not exist at some or all points on the boundary.

82

If $f(z)$ is regular not only inside $R$ but also at its boundary points and if $|f(z)| \leqslant M$ at the boundary points, we can conclude that $|f(z)| \leqslant M$ throughout $R$. This form of the argument is frequently used in applications.

## 5.2 The Phragmén–Lindelöf Extension

THEOREM C. *Suppose that* (i) $f(z)$ *is regular and* $|f(z)|$ *is one-valued in the finite domain* $D$, (ii) *for every positive* $\varepsilon$, *and in a certain inner neighbourhood of every boundary point* $\zeta$, *depending on* $\varepsilon$,

$$|f(z)| < M + \varepsilon \tag{A}$$

*then,* $|f(z)| \leqslant M$ *at every inner point of* $D$ *and equality at any inner point implies that* $f(z)$ *is constant throughout* $D$.

Let $G$ be the upper bound of $|f(z)|$ inside $D$, where $G = +\infty$ is not excluded as a possibility; then there are inner points $z_\lambda$ such that $|f(z_\lambda)| \to G$.

(1) Suppose that a limiting point $\bar{z}$ of $z_\lambda$ is an inner point of $D$ and consider some part of the sequence of the $z_\lambda$ tending to $\bar{z}$. Then, since $|f(z)|$ is continuous inside $D$

$$\lim_{\lambda \to \infty} |f(z_\lambda)| = |f(\bar{z})| = G.$$

In other words $|f(z)|$ assumes its maximum at an inner point $\bar{z}$ and so, by Theorem A, $|f(z)|$ is constant throughout $D$.

(2) Now suppose that all the limiting points of the sequence $z_\lambda$ are boundary points and that $\bar{z}$ is the limiting boundary point of a part of the sequence $z_\lambda$. By (A) there is a square $S$, centre $\bar{z}$, such that $|f(z)| < M + \varepsilon$ in the common part of $S$ and $D$. Since for sufficiently large $\lambda$ the points $z_\lambda$ tending to $\bar{z}$ are all in $S$, $G \leqslant M + \varepsilon$. Since $\varepsilon$ is arbitrary, $G \leqslant M$ which proves (i). Then (ii) follows by Theorem A.

## 5.3 Deductions from the Maximum-Modulus Principle

(I) *Schwarz's Lemma.* This theorem has already been proved in § 3.7.

(II) *Hadamard's Three Circles Theorem.* Let $0 < r_1 < r_2 < r_3$ and suppose that $f(z)$ is regular in the annulus $r_1 \leqslant |z| \leqslant r_3$. If $M_1, M_2, M_3$ are the maxima of $|f(z)|$ on the three circles $|z| = r_1, r_2, r_3$

*respectively, then*

$$a_{31} \log M_2 \leqslant a_{32} \log M_1 + a_{21} \log M_3, \tag{1}$$

*where*

$$a_{ij} = \log \frac{r_i}{r_j}.$$

If $f(z)$ is constant then the equality sign holds in (1). $M_1, M_2, M_3$ must be positive so long as $f(z)$ is non-zero. For any real number $p$, $z^p$ is not, in general, one-valued but $|z^p f(z)|$ is one-valued and continuous. On $|z| = r_1$, $|z^p f(z)| \leqslant r_1^p M_1$ and on $|z| = r_3$ we have $|z^p f(z)| \leqslant r_3^p M_3$ and so on the boundary of the annulus

$$|z^p f(z)| \leqslant \max(r_1^p M_1, r_3^p M_3). \tag{2}$$

But $\phi(z) = z^p f(z)$ is regular in the annulus and so the maximum of $|\phi(z)|$ occurs on one of the bounding circles, hence

$$|\phi(z)| \leqslant \max(r_1^p M_1, r_3^p M_3)$$

or, on $|z| = r_2$,

$$|f(z)| \leqslant \max(r_1^p r_2^{-p} M_1, r_3^p r_2^{-p} M_3). \tag{3}$$

But $p$ is at our choice, and we choose it so that the two numbers in the bracket in (3) are equal, i.e. so that

$$r_1^p M_1 = r_3^p M_3$$

or

$$p = -\left(\log \frac{M_3}{M_1}\right) \bigg/ \left(\log \frac{r_3}{r_1}\right) = -\left(\log \frac{M_3}{M_1}\right) \bigg/ a_{31}.$$

With this value of $p$, (3) becomes

$$M_2 \leqslant \left(\frac{r_2}{r_1}\right)^{-p} M_1.$$

On taking logarithms

$$\log M_2 = -p \log \frac{r_2}{r_1} + \log M_1$$

$$= \frac{a_{21}}{a_{31}} \log \frac{M_3}{M_1} + \log M_1,$$

so that

$$a_{31} \log M_2 = a_{21} \log M_3 + (a_{31} - a_{21}) \log M_1$$

and since

$$a_{31} - a_{21} = \log \frac{r_3}{r_1} - \log \frac{r_2}{r_1} = \log \frac{r_3}{r_2} = a_{32},$$

the result follows.

A convex function† in a given interval is defined as follows. If for every pair of unequal values $t_1$, $t_2$ in the interval,

$$\phi\{\tfrac{1}{2}(t_1 + t_2)\} \leqslant \tfrac{1}{2}\phi(t_1) + \tfrac{1}{2}\phi(t_2)$$

then $\phi(t)$ is convex in the interval. Since for a differentiable convex function $\phi'(t)$ is increasing, if $t$ be any value between $t_1$ and $t_2$ the condition may be written

$$\frac{\phi(t) - \phi(t_1)}{t - t_1} < \frac{\phi(t_2) - \phi(t)}{t_2 - t}.$$

Hence if $f(x)$ is a convex function and $x_1 < x_2 < x_3$ we have

$$f(x_2) = \frac{x_3 - x_2}{x_3 - x_1} f(x_1) + \frac{x_2 - x_1}{x_3 - x_1} f(x_3).$$

Since Hadamard's theorem can be written,

$$\log M(r_2) \leqslant \frac{\log r_3 - \log r_2}{\log r_3 - \log r_1} \log M(r_1) + \frac{\log r_2 - \log r_1}{\log r_3 - \log r_1} \log M(r_3)$$

this is equivalent to stating that $\log M(r)$ is a convex function of $\log r$.

### 5.4

(III) *Hardy's Theorem on* $I(r)$. *If*

$$I(r) = \frac{1}{2\pi} \int\limits_0^{2\pi} |f(re^{i\theta})| \, d\theta,$$

*then, if* $f(z)$ *is regular and not a constant in* $|z| < R$, $I(r)$ *steadily increases with* $r$ *and* $\log I(r)$ *is a convex function of* $\log r$.

† See my *Course of Analysis*, p. 152, referred to as *P.A.* hereafter.

Suppose that $0 < r_1 < r_2 < r_3$ and define $\phi(\theta)$, $0 \leqslant \theta \leqslant 2\pi$, and $F(z)$ by

$$\phi(\theta)f(r_2 e^{i\theta}) = |f(r_2 e^{i\theta})|, \quad F(z) = \frac{1}{2\pi} \int\limits_0^{2\pi} f(z e^{i\theta})\phi(\theta)\,d\theta.$$

Since $F(z)$ is regular in and on $|z| = r_3$ we may suppose that it attains its maximum modulus at $r_3 e^{i\theta_3}$. Then

$$I(r_2) = F(r_2) \leqslant |F(r_3 e^{i\theta_3})| \leqslant I(r_3)$$

which proves that $I(r)$ increases.

Now choose $p$ by the condition $r_1^p I(r_1) = r_3^p I(r_3)$. The function $z^p F(z)$ is regular in the ring space $r_1 \leqslant z \leqslant r_3$ and its modulus is one-valued. Hence, by Theorem A,

$$r_2^p I(r_2) = r_2^p F(r_2) \leqslant \max_{r_1 \leqslant |z| \leqslant r_3} |z^p F(z)| \leqslant r_1^p I(r_1) = r_3^p I(r_3),$$

and the result follows as in Theorem (II).

### 5.5

(IV) *A Theorem on the Number of Zeros of a Bounded Function. Let $f(z)$ be regular and $|f(z)| \leqslant M$ in the circle $|z| \leqslant R$, $|f(0)| = a \neq 0$. Then the number of zeros of $f(z)$ in $|z| \leqslant \frac{1}{3}R$ cannot exceed $A \log(M/a)$.*
Suppose $z_1, z_2, \ldots, z_n$ are the zeros of $f(z)$ in $|z| \leqslant \frac{1}{3}R$. If

$$g(z) = f(z) \bigg/ \prod_{m=1}^{n} \left(1 - \frac{z}{z_m}\right),$$

then $g(z)$ is regular for $|z| \leqslant R$ and on $|z| = R$ we have $|z/z_m| \geqslant 3$ for $m = 1, 2, \ldots, n$. Hence

$$|g(z)| \leqslant M \bigg/ \prod_{m=1}^{n} (3-1) = \frac{M}{2^n}$$

for $|z| = R$ and so also for $|z| < R$. In particular the theorem is true for $z = 0$. Since $g(0) = f(0)$,

$$a = |f(0)| \leqslant \frac{M}{2^n}$$

whence

$$n \leqslant \frac{1}{\log 2} \log \frac{M}{a}$$

and this is the required result, putting $A$ for $(\log 2)^{-1}$.

The factor $\frac{1}{3}$ can clearly be replaced by any number less than $\frac{1}{2}$.

### 5.6

(V) *Carathéodory's Inequality.* Let $f(z)$ be a regular function in $|z| \leqslant R$ and let $M(r)$ and $A(r)$ denote the maxima of $|f(z)|$ and $\mathscr{R}f(z)$ on $|z| = r$. Then for $0 < r < R$,

$$M(r) \leqslant \frac{R+r}{R-r}\{A(R)+|f(0)|\}.$$

Suppose first that $f(0) = 0$ and let $g(z) = f(z)/\{2A(R)-f(z)\}$. Now $g(z)$ is regular for $|z| \leqslant R$ since the real part of its denominator is not zero, $g(0) = 0$, and if $f(z) = u+iv$

$$|g(z)|^2 = \frac{u^2+v^2}{\{2A(R)-u\}^2+v^2} \leqslant 1,$$

since $u \leqslant 2A(R)-u$. Hence by Schwarz's lemma, § 3.7, $|g(z)| \leqslant r/R$; hence

$$|f(z)| = \left|\frac{2A(R)g(z)}{1-g(z)}\right| \leqslant \frac{2A(R)r}{R-r} < \frac{R+r}{R-r}A(R).$$

If $f(0) \neq 0$ apply the above result to $f(z)-f(0)$, then

$$|f(z)-f(0)| \leqslant \frac{2r}{R-r} \max_{|z|=R} \mathscr{R}\{f(z)-f(0)\} \leqslant \frac{2r}{R-r}\{A(R)+|f(0)|\}.$$

Hence

$$|f(z)| \leqslant \frac{2r}{R-r}\{A(r)+|f(0)|\}+|f(0)| \leqslant \frac{R+r}{R-r}\{A(R)+|f(0)|\}.$$

For further details the reader may refer to larger treatises.†

† See Titchmarsh, *Theory of Functions*, Ch. V, *et al.*

## Examples 5

**1.** The function $f(z)$ is regular inside and on a simple closed contour $C$ and $|f(z)| \geqslant m$ on $C$. If there is a point $c$ within $C$ such that $|f(c)| < m$, prove that there is a zero of $f(z)$ within $C$.

Deduce that every polynomial equation has at least one root.

**2.** The function $f(z)$ is regular and on the unit circle $|z| = 1$, $|f(z)| \leqslant M$ on $|z| = 1$ but there is an arc of the circumference of length $2\pi k/n$ on which $|f(z)| \leqslant m < M$, where $k$ and $n$ are positive integers ($k < n$). By considering

$$\prod_{r=1}^{n} f\{z \exp(2\pi irk/n)\}$$

or otherwise, show that

$$|f(0)| \leqslant M\left(\frac{m}{M}\right)^{k/n}.$$

**3.** (i) If $f(z)$ is regular in the closed circle $|z| \leqslant R$ and if $f(0) = 0$ show that either $f(z)/z$ is constant for $0 < |z| \leqslant R$ or $|f(z)/z| < M(r)/r$, whenever $0 < |z| < r \leqslant R$, where $M(r) = \max|f(z)|$ on $|z| = r$.

(ii) If $f(z)$ satisfies $|f(z)| \leqslant 1$ for $|z| \leqslant 1$ and if further $f(0) = 0$ and $f(1) = 1$ show that $|f'(1)| \geqslant 1$.

**4.** If $f(z)$ and $g(z)$ are regular and not constant in a domain $D$ show that the function $\phi(z) = |f(z)| + |g(z)|$ assumes its maximum at a boundary point of $D$. Show that the same is true of $\psi(z) = |f(z)|^p + |g(z)|^q$ for $p, q > 0$.

**5.** The function $f(z)$ is regular in $|z| < 1$ and satisfies $|f(z)| \leqslant M$. If $f(0) = a$, apply Schwarz's lemma to the function

$$\frac{M\{f(z) - a\}}{M^2 - \bar{a}f(z)}$$

to show that, if $|z| \leqslant r < 1$

$$\frac{M - f(z)}{1 - r} \geqslant \frac{M(M - |a|)}{M + r|a|}.$$

**6.** A function $f(z)$ is regular in and on the contour $C$, $|z| = 1$, and $|f(z)| \leqslant M$ on $C$. If $|a| < 1$ and if

$$F(z) = \frac{1 - \bar{a}z}{a - z} f(z),$$

show that $|F(z)| \leqslant M$ on $C$. Deduce that if $f(a) = 0$,

$$|f(z)| \leqslant M\left|\frac{z - a}{\bar{a}z - 1}\right|$$

within $C$.

**7.** The function $f(z)$ is regular for $|z| \leqslant 1$ and non-zero for $|z| < 1$. On $|z| = 1$ $|f(z)| = M > 0$. Prove that $f(z)$ is constant for $|z| \leqslant 1$.

The functions $f(z)$ and $g(z)$ are regular and non-zero for $|z| \leqslant 1$. On $|z| = 1$ we have $|f(z)| = |g(z)|$ and $f(0)$, $g(0)$ are both real and positive. Show that $f(z) = g(z)$ throughout $|z| \leqslant 1$.

(Consider the function $\phi(z) = f(z)/g(z)$.)

**8.** If $f(z)$ is a polynomial of degree $n$ such that $|f(z)| \leqslant M(r_i)$ on the circle $|z| = r_i$ ($i = 1$ or $2$) show that

$$\frac{M(r_1)}{r_1^n} \geqslant \frac{M(r_2)}{r_2^n}$$

when $r_1 < r_2$.

Under what circumstances can equality hold?

**9.** If $f(z)$ is regular for $r_1 < |z| < r_2$ and

$$I_2(r) = \frac{1}{2\pi} \int\limits_0^{2\pi} |f(re^{i\theta})|^2 \, d\theta,$$

show that $\log I_2(r)$ is a convex function of $\log r$ for $r_1 < r < r_2$.

If

$$f(z) = \sum_{n=1}^{\infty} \frac{z^n + z^{-n}}{2^n}$$

show that, for $\frac{1}{2} < r < 2$, $I_2(r) \geqslant \frac{2}{3}$.

**10.** If $f(z)$ is regular for $|z| \leqslant R$ and has a zero of order $m$ at the origin and if $|f(z)| \leqslant M$ on the circle $|z| = R$, show that, when $|z| = \rho < R$,

$$|f(z)| < M\left(\frac{\rho}{R}\right)^m \quad \text{and} \quad |f^{(m)}(0)| \leqslant \frac{m!\,M}{R^m}.$$

$F(z)$ is regular for $|z| \leqslant R$ and has a simple zero at $z = 0$. On the upper half of the circle $|z| = R$, $|F(z)| \leqslant M$ and on the lower half of the circle $|F(z)| \leqslant N$. By considering the function $F(z)F(-z)$, or otherwise, show that

$$|F'(0)| \leqslant \sqrt{(MN)}/R.$$

**11.** A function $f(z)$ is regular for $|z| \leqslant 1$, $|f(z)| \leqslant 1$ for $|z| = 1$ and $f(\frac{1}{2}) = f(-\frac{1}{2}) = 0$. Prove that for $|z| = r < 1$

$$|f(z)| \leqslant \left|\frac{4z^2 - 1}{z^2 - 4}\right| \leqslant \frac{4r^2 + 1}{r^2 + 4}.$$

**12.** $f(z)$ is regular and $|f(z)| < 1$ for $|z| < 1$. Let $|f(0)| = \lambda$. Show that, if $0 < |z| < 1$,

$$|f(z) - f(0)| \leqslant |z|\frac{1 - \lambda^2}{1 - \lambda|z|}.$$

**13.** If $0 < r_1 < r_2$ and $f(z)$ is regular in $r_1 \leqslant |z| \leqslant r_2$, given that $|f(z)| \leqslant h$ on $|z| = r_1$ and $|f(z)| \leqslant k$ on $|z| = r_2$, prove that on $|z| = \sqrt{(r_1 r_2)}$

$$|f(z)| \leqslant \sqrt{(hk)}.$$

**14.** A function $f(z)$ is regular inside and on the boundary of the square $-1 \leqslant x \leqslant 1$, $-1 \leqslant y \leqslant 1$ ($z = x + iy$), except for simple poles at $z = \pm 1$ and $|f(z)| \leqslant M/|y|$ on the boundary. By considering $F(z) = (1 - z^2)f(z)$, or otherwise, show that, on the imaginary axis, for $|y| \leqslant 1$,

$$|f(iy)| < \sqrt{5M/(1 + y^2)} \tag{Liv.}$$

7

CHAPTER 6

# INTEGRAL FUNCTIONS

## 6.1 Definition and Preliminaries

An Integral Function is a function defined by a Taylor series with infinite radius of convergence, $f(z) = \Sigma a_n z^n$. The radius of convergence is infinite if $\lim a_n^{1/n} = 0$. Such functions have no singularities at any finite point, but have an isolated essential singularity at infinity, e.g.

$$\sin z = z - \frac{z^3}{3!} + \ldots$$

is an integral function, the principal part at $\infty$ being an infinite series.†

An integral function may be regarded as an infinite polynomial and so the next simplest type of function to a polynomial, but any attempt to extend results valid for polynomials to integral functions fails because of two simple facts: (i) a polynomial $P(z)$ of degree $n$ is such that $P(z) = k$ has a root, in other words $P(z)$ assumes every value; and (ii)

$$P(z) = c(z - z_1) \ldots (z - z_n),$$

is the product of $n$ linear factors.

The integral function $e^z$ does not take the value 0, so (i) does not necessarily hold. Further, if $z_1, z_2, \ldots, z_n, \ldots$ are the zeros of an integral function, the product

$$\prod_1^\infty \left(1 - \frac{z}{z_n}\right),$$

may not converge and its value may not, if it does converge, be

† See *P.C.V.*, p. 103.

independent of the order of the factors. The sine product, in the form

$$\sin \pi z = \pi z \prod_{-\infty}^{\infty}{}' \left(1 - \frac{z}{n}\right) e^{z/n},$$

illustrates the fact that the integral function $\sin z$ cannot be expressed in terms of simple factors $1 - z/z_n$; there is also an exponential factor.

The most general integral function with no zeros is of the form $e^{f(z)}$ where $f(z)$ is itself an integral function. This follows from the fact that if $g(z)$ is an integral function which never vanishes then $G(z) = g'(z)/g(z)$ is also an integral function (I.F.) and, on integration along any path from $z_0$ to $z$,

$$\log g(z) = \log g(z_0) + \int_{z_0}^{z} G(z)\,dz,$$

and the right-hand side is an I.F.

## 6.2 Weierstrass's Primary Factors

The expressions

$$E(u, 0) = 1 - u, \quad E(u, p) = (1 - u)\exp\left(u + \frac{u^2}{2} + \dots + \frac{u^p}{p}\right) (p = 1, 2, \dots)$$

are called *primary factors*.

The behaviour of $E(u, p)$ as $u \to 0$ clearly depends on $p$. For $|u| < 1$,

$$\log E(u, p) = -\frac{u^{p+1}}{p+1} - \frac{u^{p+2}}{p+2} - \dots$$

Hence if $\lambda > 1$ and $|u| \leqslant 1/\lambda$,

$$|\log E(u, p)| \leqslant |u|^{p+1} + |u|^{p+2} + \dots$$

$$\leqslant |u|^{p+1}\left\{1 + \frac{1}{\lambda} + \frac{1}{\lambda^2} + \dots\right\} = \frac{\lambda}{\lambda - 1}|u|^{p+1}.$$

**Weierstrass's Theorem**

*Given any sequence of numbers $z_1, z_2, \dots$ whose only limiting point is at infinity, there exists an integral function with zeros at these points and nowhere else. The function is not, however, uniquely determined by the zeros.*

Arrange the zeros so that $|z_1| \leqslant |z_2| \leqslant \ldots$, let $|z_n| = r_n$ and $p_1, p_2, \ldots$ be a sequence of positive integers such that,

$$\sum_{n=1}^{\infty} \left(\frac{r}{r_n}\right)^{p_n}$$

is convergent for all values of $r$. We can always find such a sequence, for $r_n \to \infty$, since otherwise the zeros would have a limiting point other than $\infty$. Also we can take $p_n = n$ since, for $r_n > 2r$

$$\left(\frac{r}{r_n}\right)^n < \frac{1}{2^n}$$

and so the series is convergent when $p_n = n$.

Let

$$f(z) = \prod_{n=1}^{\infty} E\left(\frac{z}{z_n}, p_n - 1\right). \tag{1}$$

This function has the required property for, if $|z_n| > 2|z|$,

$$\left| \log E\left(\frac{z}{z_n}, p_n - 1\right) \right| \leqslant 2\left(\frac{r}{r_n}\right)^{p_n} \tag{2}$$

and so the series

$$\sum_{|z_n| > 2R} \log E\left(\frac{z}{z_n}, p_n - 1\right)$$

is uniformly convergent for $|z| \leqslant R$ and its only zeros in this region are those of

$$\prod_{|z_n| \leqslant 2R} E\left(\frac{z}{z_n}, p_n - 1\right),$$

that is the points $z_1, z_2, \ldots$ Since $R$ may be as large as we please this proves that (1) has the required property.

Since the $p_n$ are at our choice, the function $f(z)$ of (1) is not uniquely determined.

## The Factorization of an I.F.

*If $f(z)$ is an I.F. and $f(0) \neq 0$ then*

$$f(z) = f(0)P(z)\,e^{g(z)},$$

*where $P(z)$ is a product of primary factors and $g(z)$ is an I.F.*

We form $P(z)$ as in Weierstrass's theorem from the zeros of $f(z)$.

Let

$$\phi(z) = \frac{f'(z)}{f(z)} - \frac{P'(z)}{P(z)},$$

then $\phi(z)$ is an I.F., since the poles of one term are cancelled by those of the other. Hence also

$$g(z) = \int_0^z \phi(t)\, dt = \log f(z) - \log f(0) - \log P(z)$$

is an I.F. and the result follows.

If $f(z)$ has a zero of order $s$ at $z = 0$ we insert a factor $z^s$. The factorization is not unique.

### 6.3 The Order of an I.F.

An I.F., $f(z)$, is of *finite order* if there exists a real number $k$ independent of $r$, such that the maximum-modulus $M(r)$ on the circle $|z| = r$ satisfies

$$\log M(r) < r^k \tag{1}$$

for all sufficiently large $r$.

If no such $k$ exists then $f(z)$ is of *infinite order*. Clearly $k > 0$, for if $k \leqslant 0$, $M(r)$ would be bounded and so, by Liouville's theorem $f(z)$ would be a constant.

Since if (1) holds for any $k$ it also holds for all greater values of $k$, we get an upper segment† of $k$'s; this upper segment determines a unique lower bound $\rho$ of the sequence of $k$'s such that (1) holds for all sufficiently large values of $r$ when $k > \rho$, but not when $k < \rho$. This number $\rho$ is called the *order* of $f(z)$.

If $k < \rho$, $\log M(r) > r^k$ holds for a sequence of values of $r$ which increase indefinitely. Hence

$$\rho = \overline{\lim_{r \to \infty}} \frac{\log \log M(r)}{\log r}.$$

If $f(z)$ is of infinite order the right-hand side is $+\infty$.

E.g. A polynomial is of order 0, $e^z$ and $\sin z$ of order 1, but $\exp(e^z)$ is of infinite order.

† See *P.A.*, p. 29.

## 6.4 Jensen's Theorem

*Let $f(z)$ be regular for $|z| < R$, $f(0) \neq 0$ and $r_1, r_2, \ldots, r_n$ the moduli of the zeros of $f(z)$ in the circle $|z| < R$. If these moduli are arranged in ascending order, then for $r_n \leqslant r \leqslant r_{n+1}$*

$$\log \frac{r^n |f(0)|}{r_1 r_2 \ldots r_n} = \frac{1}{2\pi} \int_0^{2\pi} \log |f(r\,e^{i\theta})| \, d\theta, \tag{1}$$

*a zero of order k being counted k times.*

This theorem can be expressed in another form, which is more useful in considering its application to integral functions in particular. We define $n(x)$ to be the number of zeros of $f(z)$ for $|z| \leqslant x$, then *Jensen's theorem takes the form*:

$$\int_0^r \frac{n(x)}{x} \, dx = \frac{1}{2\pi} \int_0^{2\pi} \log |f(r\,e^{i\theta})| \, d\theta - \log |f(0)|. \tag{2}$$

For, if $r_n \leqslant r \leqslant r_{n+1}$,

$$\log \frac{r^n}{r_1 r_2 \ldots r_n} = n \log r - \sum_{m=1}^{n} \log r_m \tag{3}$$

$$= \sum_{m=1}^{n-1} m(\log r_{m+1} - \log r_m) + n(\log r - \log r_n)$$

$$= \sum_{m=1}^{n-1} m \int_{r_m}^{r_{m+1}} \frac{dx}{x} + n \int_{r_n}^{r} \frac{dx}{x}.$$

But $m = n(x)$ for $r_m \leqslant x \leqslant r_{m+1}$, $n = n(x)$ for $r_n \leqslant x < r$ so the left-hand side of (3) is equal to

$$\int_0^r \frac{n(x)}{x} \, dx.$$

We thus see that Jensen's theorem takes the form (2). To prove the theorem, we consider in turn four cases: (a) $f(z)$ has no zero in $|z| \leqslant r$; (b) $f(z)$ has one zero in $|z| < r$; (c) $f(z)$ has one zero *on* $|z| = r$; (d) $f(z)$ has $n$ zeros in $|z| < r_{n+1}$.

(a) Let $C$ be the circle $|z| = r$. Now $\log f(z)$ is regular within and on $C$ and

$$\log f(0) = \frac{1}{2\pi i} \int_C \frac{\log f(z)}{z}\, dz = \frac{1}{2\pi} \int_0^{2\pi} \log \{f(r\, e^{i\theta})\}\, d\theta. \qquad (4)$$

Since $n(x) = 0$ in this case, the theorem follows on taking real parts in (4).

(b) Let $f(z) = 1 - z/z_1$, where $z_1 = r_1\, e^{i\theta_1}$, then

$$|f(z)|^2 = \frac{r^2}{r_1^2} \left\{1 - \frac{r_1}{r} \exp i(\theta_1 - \theta)\right\}\left\{1 - \frac{r_1}{r} \exp -i(\theta_1 - \theta)\right\},$$

and so, if $r_1 < r$, so that there is one zero $z = z_1$ inside $C$,

$$\log |f(z)|^2 = 2 \log \frac{r}{r_1} - \sum_{m=1}^{\infty} \frac{1}{m}\left(\frac{r_1}{r}\right)^m \cos m(\theta_1 - \theta).$$

Since the series converges uniformly with respect to $\theta$, on integrating term-by-term we get

$$\frac{1}{2\pi} \int_0^{2\pi} \log |f(r\, e^{i\theta})|^2\, d\theta = 2 \log \frac{r}{r_1}.$$

This proves the theorem in case (b).

(c) Now let $f(z) = 1 - z/z_1$ where $|z| = r_1 = r$. Here $f(z)$ has one zero on $|z| = r$, and

$$|f(z)|^2 = \{1 - \exp i(\theta - \theta_1)\}\{1 - \exp[-i(\theta - \theta_1)]\}$$
$$= 2\{1 - \cos(\theta - \theta_1)\} = 4 \sin^2 \tfrac{1}{2}(\theta - \theta_1),$$

and so

$$\frac{1}{2\pi} \int_0^{2\pi} \log |f(r\, e^{i\theta})|\, d\theta = \frac{1}{2\pi} \int_0^{2\pi} \log |2 \sin \tfrac{1}{2}(\theta - \theta_1)|\, d\theta.$$

Call the last integral $I$. Put $\phi = \theta - \theta_1$ then

$$I = \int_{-\theta_1}^{2\pi - \theta_1} \log |2 \sin \tfrac{1}{2}\phi|\, d\phi = \int_0^{2\pi - \theta_1} + \int_{-\theta_1}^0 \log |2 \sin \tfrac{1}{2}\phi|\, d\phi.$$

By putting $\psi = 2\pi + \phi$ in the second of these,

$$I = \int_0^{2\pi - \theta_1} \log \left| 2 \sin \tfrac{1}{2}\phi \right| \, d\phi + \int_{2\pi - \theta_1}^{2\pi} \log \left| 2 \sin \tfrac{1}{2}\psi \right| \, d\psi$$

$$= \int_0^{2\pi} \log 2 \left| \sin \tfrac{1}{2}\theta \right| \, d\theta.$$

We now show that $I = 0$, for the modulus sign can now be omitted so that

$$I = \frac{1}{2\pi} \int_0^{2\pi} (\log 2 + \log \sin \tfrac{1}{2}\theta) \, d\theta = \log 2 + \frac{1}{\pi} \int_0^{\pi} \log \sin \phi \, d\phi,$$

by putting $2\phi = \theta$.
Since

$$\int_0^{\pi} \log \sin \phi \, d\phi = -\pi \log 2,$$

a well-known result, it follows that $I = 0$. This proves case (c).

(d) The remaining case, in which we put

$$f(z) = \left(1 - \frac{z}{z_1}\right) \left(1 - \frac{z}{z_2}\right) \cdots \left(1 - \frac{z}{z_n}\right) \phi(z),$$

where $\phi(z) \neq 0$ for $|z| < r_{n+1}$ and $\phi(0) = f(0)$, follows by the addition of the previous ones.

### 6.5 The Function $n(r)$ for an I.F.

In §6.3 we defined the order of an I.F. $f(z)$ in terms of the maximum-modulus $M(r)$. This may also be expressed by saying that if $f(z)$ is of finite order $\rho$

$$\log \left| f(r \, e^{i\theta}) \right| < K r^{\rho + \varepsilon}, \tag{1}$$

where $K$ depends on $\varepsilon$ only. Hence we can prove the theorem

*If $f(z)$ is of order $\rho$ then $n(r) = O(r^{\rho + \varepsilon})$.*

From (1) above, on using Jensen's theorem in the form (2) of the last paragraph, since it holds for all values of $r$ when $f(z)$ is an I.F., we have

$$\int_0^{2r} \frac{n(x)}{x} \, dx < Kr^{\rho+\varepsilon}.$$

But, since $n(r)$ is non-decreasing,

$$\int_r^{2r} \frac{n(x)}{x} \, dx \geqslant n(r) \int_r^{2r} \frac{dx}{x} = n(r) \log 2.$$

Hence

$$n(r) \leqslant \frac{1}{\log 2} \int_0^{2r} \frac{n(x)}{x} \, dx < Kr^{\rho+\varepsilon}.$$

This may be expressed loosely by saying that the higher the order of $f(z)$ the more zeros it has in a given region.

THEOREM. *If $r_1, r_2, \ldots$ are the moduli of the zeros of $f(z)$ then the series $\Sigma r_n^{-t}$ is convergent if $t > \rho$.*

Let $q$ be a number between $t$ and $\rho$; then $n(r) < Ar^q$ and on putting $r = r_n$, $n < Ar_n^q$. Hence

$$r_n^{-t} < Ar_n^{-t/q},$$

and the result is proved, since $t/q > 1$.

The lower bound of the positive numbers $t$ for which $\sum r_n^{-t}$ is convergent is called the *exponent of convergence of the zeros* of $f(z)$ and is denoted by $\rho_1$. What we have just proved is that $\rho_1 \leqslant \rho$.

If $f(z) = e^z$, $\rho = 1$ but since there are no zeros $\rho_1 = 0$.

We remark that $\rho_1 = 0$ for any function with a finite number of zeros so that $\rho_1 > 0$ implies that there is an infinity of zeros.

The exponent of convergence $\rho_1$ is given by

$$\rho_1 = \overline{\lim_{n \to \infty}} \frac{\log n}{\log r_n}.$$

We have just seen that $\sum r_n^{-t}$ is convergent if $t > \rho$, and since $\rho_1 \leqslant \rho$ the series converges when $t > \rho_1$. It is divergent if $t < \rho_1$ by definition of $\rho_1$.

If $\rho_1$ is infinite the series diverges for every real value of $t$. For in this case there exists a set of integers for which $r_n^t < n$. Let $v$ be such a value of $n$ and $\mu$ the least integer greater than $\frac{1}{2}v$. Since $r_n$ increases with $n$

$$\sum_{v-\mu}^{v} r_n^{-t} > \frac{\mu}{r_v^t} > \frac{\mu}{v} > \frac{1}{2},$$

so $\Sigma r_n^{-t}$ diverges.

Note that if $\rho_1$ is finite, the series $\Sigma r_n^{-\rho_1}$ may converge or diverge. If $r_n = n$, $\rho_1 = 1$ and $\Sigma 1/n$ is divergent. If $r_n = n(\log n)^\alpha$, where $\alpha > 1$, again $\rho_1 = 1$ but the series in this case converges. [To see that $\rho_1 = 1$, note that

$$\rho_1 = \lim_{n \to \infty} \frac{\log n}{\log r_n} = \lim \frac{\log n}{\log n + \alpha \log \log n} = 1, \quad \text{since } \frac{\log \log n}{\log n} \to 0].$$

## 6.6 Canonical Products and Genus of an I.F.

It follows from the preceding paragraph that if the I.F. $f(z)$ is of finite order, then there is an integer $p$, independent of $n$ such that

$$\prod_{n=1}^{\infty} E\left(\frac{z}{z_n}, p\right) \tag{1}$$

is convergent for all values of $z$. This is Weierstrass's primary factor of § 6.2 with $p_n = p + 1$ and the product is convergent if

$$\Sigma \left(\frac{r}{r_n}\right)^{p+1} \tag{2}$$

is convergent. This is true for all values of $r$ if $p + 1 > \rho_1$ and so true if $p + 1 > \rho$, since $\rho_1 \leqslant \rho$.

If $p$ is the smallest integer for which (2) converges then (1) is called the *canonical product* formed with the zeros of the I.F. $f(z)$ and $p$ is called its *genus*.

If $\rho_1$ is not an integer $p = [\rho_1]$; if $\rho_1$ is an integer, $p = \rho_1$ if $\Sigma r_n^{-\rho_1}$ is divergent, while $p = \rho_1 - 1$ if it is convergent. Hence $p \leqslant \rho_1 \leqslant \rho$. The genus of a given function is sometimes difficult to find. We give no further reference to it here, apart from the definition.

### 6.7 Hadamard's Theorem on I.F. of Finite Order

*The function* $e^{H(z)}$ *is an integral function of finite order with no zeros if and only if $H(z)$ is a polynomial.*

We already know that if $H(z)$ is an I.F. then $e^{H(z)}$ is an I.F. with no zeros. Further if $H(z)$ is a polynomial of degree $k$, then $e^{H(z)}$ is of finite order $k$. Hence we have to prove that if $\mathscr{R}H(z) < r^{\rho+\varepsilon}$, for every positive $\varepsilon$ and all sufficiently large values of $r$, $H(z)$ is a polynomial of degree less than or equal to $\rho$.

Let $C$ be the circle $|z| = r$, then the coefficient of $z^n$ in the Taylor expansion of $H(z)$ about the point $z = 0$ is

$$a_n = \frac{1}{2\pi i} \int_C \frac{H(z)}{z^{n+1}} \, dz.$$

If $n > 0$,

$$\int_C \frac{\overline{H}(z)}{z^{n+1}} \, dz = \int_C \sum_{m=0}^{\infty} \bar{a}_m \bar{z}^m \frac{dz}{z^{n+1}} = \sum_0^{\infty} \int_0^{2\pi} \bar{a}_m r^{m-n} \, e^{-(m+n)i\theta} \, i \, d\theta,$$

and this is zero, the term-by-term integration being justified by uniform convergence. Since $2\mathscr{R}H(z) = H(z) + \overline{H}(z)$, we get

$$a_n = \frac{1}{\pi i} \int_C \mathscr{R}H(z) \frac{dz}{z^{n+1}} = \frac{1}{\pi} \int_0^{2\pi} \mathscr{R}H(re^{i\theta}) \frac{d\theta}{r^n e^{ni\theta}}.$$

Hence

$$|a_n| r^n \leqslant \frac{1}{\pi} \int_0^{2\pi} |\mathscr{R}H(re^{i\theta})| \, d\theta.$$

Also

$$a_0 = \frac{1}{2\pi i} \int_C \frac{H(z)}{z} \, dz = \frac{1}{2\pi} \int_0^{2\pi} H(re^{i\theta}) \, d\theta.$$

Hence

$$2\mathscr{R}a_0 + |a_n| r^n \leqslant \frac{1}{\pi} \int_0^{2\pi} \{\mathscr{R}H + |\mathscr{R}H|\} \, d\theta.$$

The integrand is either $2\mathscr{R}H$ or 0 according as $\mathscr{R}H > 0$ or $\leqslant 0$, and since $\mathscr{R}H < r^{\rho+\varepsilon}$ we get

$$2\mathscr{R}a_0 + |a_n|r^n < 4r^{\rho+\varepsilon} \tag{1}$$

for every positive $\varepsilon$ and all sufficiently large $r$.

(1) may be written

$$|a_n| < 4r^{\rho+\varepsilon-n} - 2\mathscr{R}a_0 r^{-n}$$

and on making $r \to \infty$ we get $a_n = 0$ if $n > \rho$.

This proves the theorem.

### 6.8 The Coefficients in the Expansion of an I.F. of Finite Order

*The necessary and sufficient condition that*

$$f(z) = \sum_{n=0}^{\infty} a_n z^n \tag{1}$$

*shall be an I.F. of finite order $\rho$ is that*

$$\varlimsup_{n \to \infty} \frac{\log |b_n|}{n \log n} = \frac{1}{\rho}, \qquad \text{where } b_n = 1/a_n.$$

Let

$$\varliminf \frac{\log |b_n|}{n \log n} = \mu,$$

where $\mu$ is zero, positive or infinite. For $n > \nu$ and every positive $\varepsilon$,

$$\log |b_n| > (\mu - \varepsilon) n \log n,$$

or

$$|a_n| < n^{-n(\mu-\varepsilon)}.$$

Now if $\mu > 0$, $|a_n|^{1/n} \to 0$ and so (1) is convergent for all $z$, so that $f(z)$ is an I.F.

First let $\mu$ be finite and $r > 1$, then

$$|f(z)| \leqslant \sum_0^{\nu} |a_n|r^n + \sum_{\nu+1}^{\infty} |a_n|r^n < Ar^\nu + \sum_{n=\nu+1}^{\infty} r^n n^{-n(\mu-\varepsilon)},$$

where $A$ is a constant.

By dividing up the last series into two parts $S_1$ and $S_2$, we can show that

$$|f(z)| < K \exp\{(2r)^k \log r\}, \tag{2}$$

where $k = 1/(\mu - \varepsilon)$.

Suppose that in $S_1$ $n \leqslant (2r)^k$, then $r^n \leqslant \exp\{(2r)^k \log r\}$.

In $S_2$ we have $rn^{-(\mu-\varepsilon)} < \frac{1}{2}$ so that $S_2 < \Sigma(\frac{1}{2})^n < 1$, which establishes (2). It follows that, for all sufficiently large $r$,

$$M(r) < \exp\{B(2r)^k \log r\}.$$

But by § 6.3

$$\rho = \varlimsup_{r \to \infty} \frac{\log \log M(r)}{\log r} \leqslant \varlimsup \frac{\log B + \log(2r)^k + \log \log r}{\log r},$$

or

$$\rho \leqslant k. \tag{3}$$

It also follows from the definition of $\mu$ that there exists an infinite number of positive integers such that

$$\log |b_n| < (\mu + \varepsilon)n \log n,$$

or

$$|a_n| > n^{-(\mu+\varepsilon)n}.$$

By Cauchy's inequality, for each such value of $n$,

$$M(r) \geqslant |a_n| r^n > \left(\frac{r}{n^{\mu+\varepsilon}}\right)^n.$$

If we take $r = 2n^{\mu+\varepsilon}$ we get for certain arbitrarily large $r$,

$$M(r) > 2^n = \exp\{(\tfrac{1}{2}r)^{k_1} \log 2\}, \qquad \text{where } k_1 = 1/(\mu + \varepsilon),$$

so that

$$\rho \geqslant k_1. \tag{4}$$

From (3) and (4), on making $\varepsilon \to 0$, we find that $\rho = 1/\mu$.

If $\mu$ is infinite, we can use the inequality

$$\log |b_n| > Kn \log n,$$

which holds for any given $K > 0$ and all sufficiently large $n$, to show that in this case the order of $f(z)$ is zero.

By means of this theorem we have established that the order of the I.F. $f(z)$ is given by

$$\rho = \varlimsup_{n \to \infty} \frac{n \log n}{\log |b_n|},$$

where $b_n = 1/a_n$.

For further details the reader must consult larger treatises.†

## Examples 6

**1.** Prove this more general form of Jensen's theorem (§ 6.4): Let $f(z)$ be meromorphic in a circle $C$, regular on $C$ and having no zeros on $C$. Let $a_1, a_2, \ldots, a_n$ be the zeros, $b_1, b_2, \ldots b_m$ the poles of $f(z)$ within $C$ (multiple poles and zeros being counted multiply); $z = 0$ is neither pole nor zero of $f(z)$.

If $f(z) = Re^{i\phi}$ prove that

$$\frac{1}{2\pi} \int_0^{2\pi} \log R \, d\theta = \log |f(0)| + \log \left| r^{n-m} \frac{b_1 b_2 \ldots b_m}{a_1 a_2 \ldots a_n} \right|,$$

where $z = re^{i\theta}$.

(This reduces to the theorem of § 6.4 when $f(z)$ is regular inside $C$. See Goursat, *Cours d'Analyse*, II, § 308.)

**2.** Find the orders of the integral functions ($p > 0$):

   (i) $\sum_0^\infty \dfrac{z^n}{(n!)^p}$      (ii) $\sum \dfrac{\cosh \sqrt{n}}{n!} z^n$      (iii) $\sum_1^\infty \dfrac{1}{(n!)^3} \left(\dfrac{z}{n}\right)^n$      (iv) $\sum_{n=1}^\infty \dfrac{(n-1)!}{(2n-1)!} z^n.$

Show that (ii) has an infinite number of zeros, all real and negative.

(Use Stirling's formula for $n!$)

**3.** Use Jensen's theorem to show that if $f(z)$ is an integral function of order $\rho$ whose only zeros are simple zeros at $z = 1^s, 2^s, \ldots, n^s, \ldots (s > 0)$ then $\rho s \geqslant 1$.

**4.** If $M(r)$ is the maximum value of $|f(z)|$ on $|z| = r$, show that if

$$f(z) = \sum_1^\infty \left(\frac{z}{n}\right)^n,$$

then, for sufficiently large $r$,

$$\frac{1}{e} \leqslant \frac{\log M(r)}{r} \leqslant 1.$$

**5.** If $f(z)$ be regular and $|f(z)| \leqslant M$ in the circle $|z| \leqslant R$, $f(0) \neq 0$ and $|f(0)| = k$ use Jensen's theorem (or otherwise) to show that the number of zeros of $f(z)$ in $|z| \leqslant \lambda R$ ($0 < \lambda < 1$) cannot exceed

$$\frac{1}{\log 1/\lambda} \log \frac{M}{k}.$$

(See § 5.5.)

---

† See, e.g., Titchmarsh, *Theory of Functions*, Ch. VIII; Copson, *Functions of a Complex Variable*, Ch. VII.

**6.** The integral function $g(z)$ is of finite order $\rho$. If $\mu(r)$ is the maximum modulus of $g'(z)$ on $|z| = r$, show that, if $R > r$

$$\frac{M(r) - |g(0)|}{r} \leqslant \mu(r) \leqslant \frac{M(R)}{R - r}.$$

Deduce that $g'(z)$ is of order $\rho$.

**7.** If

$$f(z) = \sum_{n=0}^{\infty} a_n z^n$$

is an integral function show that

$$a_n = \frac{1}{2\pi r^n} \int_0^{2\pi} f(re^{i\theta}) e^{-ni\theta}\, d\theta,$$

where $r$ is any positive number. If $u$ is the real part of $f(z)$, show that, for $n \geqslant 1$,

$$a_n = \frac{1}{\pi r^n} \int_0^{2\pi} u(re^{i\theta}) e^{-ni\theta}\, d\theta$$

and deduce that, if $u$ is never negative on $|z| = r$,

$$|a_n| \leqslant 2r^{-n} \mathcal{R} a_0.$$

(Compare *P.C.V.*, Ex. IV, 1.)

**8.** If $f(z)$ is an integral function such that $|f(z)| < M$ for every finite $z$, use Schwarz's lemma on the function

$$\frac{f(Rw) - f(0)}{2M}$$

for the circle $|w| = 1$, and show, by making $R \to \infty$, that $f(z)$ is a constant.

**9.** The maximum modulus of an integral function $f(z) = \Sigma a_n z^n$ on the circle $|z| = \rho$ is $M(\rho)$ and $f(z)$ is such that for arbitrarily small $\varepsilon$, $\rho(\varepsilon)$ can be found such that $M(\rho) < \exp(\varepsilon \rho)$ for all values of $\rho > \rho(\varepsilon)$. Prove that $\Sigma n! a_n z^n$ is also an integral function.

**10.** If $M(r)$ is the maximum modulus of the integral function $f(z)$ on $|z| = r$ and $0 < \alpha < 1$ show that, when $\alpha$ is a constant,

$$\lim_{r \to \infty} \frac{M(\alpha r)}{M(r)}$$

is zero unless $f(z)$ is a polynomial of degree $n$. In the latter case show that the limit is $\alpha^n$.

**11.** If $0 < |a_1| < |a_2| < \ldots < |a_n| < \ldots$ and $n/|a_n| \to 0$ as $n \to \infty$, show that

$$f(z) = \prod_{n=1}^{\infty} \left(1 - \frac{z^2}{a_n^2}\right)$$

is an integral function of order $\leqslant 1$, which satisfies $|f(z)| < \exp(\varepsilon |z|)$ for all values of $|z|$ which exceed some $r_0(\varepsilon)$.

**12.** $f(z)$ is an integral function with simple zeros at $z = 1, 2, 3, \ldots, n, \ldots$ and no other zeros. Show that $f(z)$ cannot satisfy an inequality of the form $|f(z)| < \exp(k|z|)$ where $0 < k < 1$, for all values of $|z|$ which exceed an assignable value. (Use Jensen's theorem.)

**13.** A function $f(z)$ is regular in $|z| < 1$, continuous in $|z| \leqslant 1$ and satisfies $0 < m \leqslant |f(z)| \leqslant M$ on $|z| = 1$. The only zeros of $f(z)$ in $|z| < 1$ are $z_1, z_2, \ldots, z_n$, all simple and lying in $|z| \leqslant \frac{1}{2}$. Show that, except at these zeros

$$m(\tfrac{2}{3})^n|z - z_1||z - z_2| \ldots |z - z_n| < |f(z)| < M2^n|z - z_1||z - z_2| \ldots |z - z_n|$$

in $|z| < 1$, unless $f$ is of the form

$$f(z) = K(z - z_1)(z - z_2) \ldots (z - z_n). \tag{Liv.}$$

## CHAPTER 7

# EXPANSIONS IN INFINITE SERIES

### 7.1 Lagrange's Expansion

Let $f(z)$ be a regular function in a domain $D$ which includes the point $z = a$. The equation,

$$F(z) = z - a - \lambda f(z) = 0, \tag{1}$$

where $\lambda$ is a variable parameter, has the root $z = a$ if $\lambda = 0$. Suppose $\lambda \neq 0$ and let $C$ be a circle of centre $a$ and radius $r$ within $D$, such that on this circle $|\lambda f(z)| < r$. By Rouché's theorem,† $F(z) = 0$ has the same number of roots inside $C$ as $z - a = 0$; hence it has only one root, $z = b$, say. Let $G(z)$ be a function regular in $C$. The function $G(z)/F(z)$ has a simple pole at $z = b$, within $C$ and the residue at that pole is $G(b)/F'(b)$. Hence

$$\frac{G(b)}{F'(b)} = \frac{1}{2\pi i} \int_C \frac{G(z)}{F(z)} \, dz = \frac{1}{2\pi i} \int_C \frac{G(z) \, dz}{z - a - \lambda f(z)}.$$

Let us use the identity,

$$\frac{1}{z - a - \lambda f(z)} = \frac{1}{z - a} + \frac{\lambda f(z)}{(z - a)^2} + \dots$$

$$+ \frac{(\lambda f(z))^n}{(z - a)^{n+1}} + \frac{1}{z - a - \lambda f(z)} \left\{ \frac{\lambda f(z)}{z - a} \right\}^{n+1}.$$

Substituting in the integral we get

$$\frac{G(b)}{F'(b)} = J_0 + \lambda J_1 + \dots + \lambda^n J_n + R_{n+1},$$

where

$$J_k = \frac{1}{2\pi i} \int_C \frac{\{f(z)\}^k G(z) \, dz}{(z - a)^{k+1}} \qquad (k = 0, 1, 2, \dots n)$$

† *P.C.V.*, p. 108.

and

$$R_{n+1} = \frac{1}{2\pi i} \int_C \frac{G(z)}{z-a-\lambda f(z)} \left\{ \frac{\lambda f(z)}{z-a} \right\}^{n+1} dz.$$

If $m$ is the maximum value of $|\lambda f(z)|$ on $C$, by hypothesis $m < r$. If $N$ is maximum of $|G(z)|$ on $C$ we have

$$|R_{n+1}| < \frac{1}{2\pi} \left( \frac{m}{r} \right)^{n+1} \frac{2\pi rN}{r-m}$$

which shows that $R_{n+1} \to 0$ as $n \to \infty$. The other coefficients are

$$J_0 = G(a), \ldots, J_n = \frac{1}{n!} \frac{d^n}{da^n} [\{f(a)\}^n G(a)].$$

Hence

$$\frac{G(b)}{F'(b)} = G(a) + \sum_{n=1}^{\infty} \frac{\lambda^n}{n!} \frac{d^n}{da^n} [G(a)\{f(a)\}^n], \tag{2}$$

where $F'(b) = 1 - \lambda f'(b)$.

This is one form of Lagrange's expansion.

Another form is obtained as follows. Let $\phi(z)$ be a function regular in $D$; then put $G(z) = \phi(z)\{1 - \lambda f'(z)\}$; when we do this, the left-hand side reduces to $\phi(b)$ and does not depend on $\lambda$. In the series on the right-hand side there will be two terms of degree $n$ in $\lambda$,

$$\frac{\lambda^n}{n!} \frac{d^n}{da^n} [\phi(a)\{f(a)\}^n] - \frac{\lambda^n}{(n-1)!} \frac{d^{n-1}}{da^{n-1}} [\phi(a)\{f(a)\}^{n-1} f'(a)],$$

which simplifies to

$$\frac{\lambda^n}{n!} \frac{d^{n-1}}{da^{n-1}} [\phi'(a)\{f(a)\}^n].$$

We thus obtain Lagrange's formula in the form

$$\phi(b) = \phi(a) + \lambda \phi'(a) f(a) + \ldots + \frac{\lambda^n}{n!} \frac{d^{n-1}}{da^{n-1}} [\phi'(a)\{f(a)\}^n] + \ldots \tag{3}$$

We have assumed that on $C$, $|\lambda f(z)| < r$, and this will be the case if $|\lambda|$ is small enough. To find the maximum value of $|\lambda|$, consider the case in which $f(z)$ is a polynomial or an integral function.

If $M(r)$ is the maximum value of $|f(z)|$ on the circle $C$ of radius $r$ and centre $a$, the proof above applies to this circle provided $|\lambda|M(r) < r$. Hence we require to find the maximum value of $r/M(r)$ as $r$ varies from 0 to $\infty$. This ratio is zero for $r = 0$, for if $M(r)$ tended to zero with $r$, $z = a$ would be a zero of $f(z)$ and $F(z)$ would be divisible by a factor $z - a$. This ratio is also zero as $r \to \infty$ for otherwise $f(z)$ would be a polynomial of the first degree. Hence $r/M(r)$ has a maximum value $\mu$ for some value $r_1$ of $r$. Hence eqn. (1) has one and only one root of modulus less than $r_1$ provided that $|\lambda| < \mu$. The expansions (2) or (3) are thus valid provided $|\lambda| \leqslant \mu$, so long as $G(z)$ and $\phi(z)$ are regular within the circle of radius $r$.

In particular, if $\phi(z) = z$, (3) becomes

$$b = a + \sum_1^\infty \frac{\lambda^n}{n!} \frac{d^{n-1}}{da^{n-1}} \{f(z)\}^n,$$

where $b$ is that root of $z = a + \lambda f(z)$ which has the value $a$ when $\lambda = 0$. As an example, the equation $z - a - \lambda z^{-1} = 0$ has one root $b$ inside the contour surrounding $a$, defined by $|z(z-a)| > \lambda$, where $\lambda < \frac{1}{2}|a|$. Here $f(z) = 1/z$ and the expansion is

$$b = a + \sum_1^\infty \frac{(-1)^{n-1}(2n-2)!}{n!(n-1)!a^{2n-1}} \lambda^n.$$

The quadratic $z^2 - az - \lambda = 0$ has two roots, but only the root $\frac{1}{2}a + \sqrt{[(a^2/4)+\lambda]}$ is represented by the expansion, the other root being outside the given contour.

### 7.2 Teixeira's Theorem

This theorem deals with the expansion of one function in positive and negative powers of another function. It is an analogue of Laurent's theorem, which expands $f(z)$ in positive and negative powers of $z$.

*Let a function $f(z)$ be regular in the annulus $R$ between an outer curve $C$ and an inner curve $C'$. Let $\phi(z)$ be regular in and on $C$ and have a simple zero at $z = a$ inside $C$. Suppose that* (i) *$\zeta$ is a given point in $R$ and* (ii) *for all points $z$ of $C$, $|\phi(\zeta)| < |\phi(z)|$, and for all* *points of $C'$, $|\phi(\zeta)| > |\phi(z)|$ then*

$$f(\zeta) = \sum_{n=0}^{\infty} A_n \{\phi(\zeta)\}^n + \sum_{n=1}^{\infty} B_n \{\phi(\zeta)\}^{-n},$$

*with the values of $A_n$, $B_n$ determined as below.*

We show first that $\phi(z) - \phi(\zeta) = 0$ has a single root $z = \zeta$ inside $C$.

$$\frac{1}{2\pi i} \int_C \frac{\phi'(z)\,dz}{\phi(z) - \phi(\zeta)} = \frac{1}{2\pi i} \left[ \int_C \frac{\phi'(z)}{\phi(z)}\,dz + \phi(\zeta) \int_C \frac{\phi'(z)\,dz}{\{\phi(z)\}^2} + \cdots \right],$$

$$= \frac{1}{2\pi i} \int_C \frac{\phi'(z)}{\phi(z)}\,dz.$$

Hence the number of roots of $\phi(z) - \phi(\zeta) = 0$ is the same as that of $\phi(z) = 0$ inside $C$, by § 1.2, Theorem A. The term-by-term integration is justified by the uniform convergence of $\Sigma \{\phi(\zeta)/\phi(z)\}^n$ on $C$.

By applying Cauchy's theorem we get

$$f(\zeta) = \frac{1}{2\pi i} \int_C \frac{f(z)\phi'(z)}{\phi(z) - \phi(\zeta)}\,dz - \frac{1}{2\pi i} \int_{C'} \frac{f(z)\phi'(z)}{\phi(z) - \phi(\zeta)}\,dz.$$

Just as in Laurent's theorem,† the first integral gives,

$$\sum_{n=0}^{\infty} \{\phi(\zeta)\}^n \int_C \frac{f(z)\phi'(z)}{\{\phi(z)\}^{n+1}}\,dz,$$

with a similar result for the second, giving

$$f(\zeta) = \sum_{n=0}^{\infty} A_n \{\phi(\zeta)\}^n + \sum_{n=1}^{\infty} B_n \{\phi(\zeta)\}^{-n},$$

where

$$A_n = \frac{1}{2\pi i} \int_C \frac{f(z)\phi'(z)\,dz}{\{\phi(z)\}^{n+1}}, \quad B_n = \frac{1}{2\pi i} \int_{C'} f(z)\{\phi(z)\}^{n-1}\phi'(z)\,dz.$$

On integration by parts we get, if $n \neq 0$,

$$A_n = \frac{1}{2\pi n i} \int_C \frac{f'(z)\,dz}{\{\phi(z)\}^n}, \quad B_n = \frac{-1}{2\pi n i} \int_{C'} \{\phi(z)\}^n f'(z)\,dz.$$

† *P.G.V.*, p. 97.

These integrals can be evaluated by the residue theorem if the poles and zeros of $f(z)$ and $\phi(z)$ inside $C$ are known.

Lagrange's expansion may be deduced from this. If we suppose that $f(z)$ is regular at all points inside $C$ and we put $\phi(\zeta) = (\zeta - a)\theta(\zeta)$, then $\theta(\zeta)$ is regular and not zero on or inside $C$ and the contour $C'$ is not required. The formulae for $A_n$ and $B_n$ now become

$$A_n = \frac{1}{2n\pi i} \int\limits_C \frac{f'(z)\,dz}{(z-a)^n\{\theta(z)\}^n}$$

$$= \frac{1}{n!}\frac{d^{n-1}}{da^{n-1}}\left\{\frac{f'(a)}{\theta^n(a)}\right\} \quad (n \geq 1), \quad A_0 = f(a), \, B_n = 0.$$

If now we write $\theta(z) = 1/\psi(z)$

$$f(\zeta) = f(a) + \sum_{n=1}^{\infty} \frac{\lambda^n}{n!}\frac{d^{n-1}}{da^{n-1}}[f'(a)\{\psi(a)\}^n],$$

which is the same as § 7.1 (3), with $f$ for $\phi$, $\zeta$ for $b$, $\psi$ for $f$.

### 7.3 Mittag–Leffler's Theorem

It is possible to construct a function which is meromorphic over the whole plane. If the moduli of the simple poles of the required function at $a_1, a_2, a_3, \ldots$, say, are arranged in ascending order, we require only that for some integer $n$, $\sum_{r=1}^{\infty} 1/a_r^n$ shall be absolutely convergent.

Consider the function $\sum_{r=1}^{\infty} w_r(z)$, where,

$$w_r(z) = \frac{1}{z-a_r} + \frac{1}{a_r} + \frac{z}{a_r^2} + \ldots + \frac{z^{n-2}}{a_r^{n-1}} = \frac{z^{n-1}}{a_r^{n-1}}\frac{1}{z-a_r}$$

If $C$ is the circle $|z| = R$, where $R < |a_{p+1}|$, then for all points $z$ in the region bounded by $C$,

$$\left|\frac{z}{a_r} - 1\right| \geq k, \quad \text{where } k = 1 - \frac{R}{|a_{p+1}|} \quad (r = p+1, p+2, \ldots).$$

Hence

$$|w_r(z)| \leq \frac{R^{n-1}}{k} \cdot \frac{1}{|a_r|^n} \quad (r = p+1, p+2, \ldots),$$

so that $\sum\limits_{r=1}^{\infty} w_r(z)$ is absolutely and uniformly convergent in the region bounded by $C$. $R$ can always be chosen large enough for any assigned point to lie in the region, and so the series $\sum\limits_{r=1}^{\infty} w_r(z)$ represents a function of the required type.

If the residues of a function $f(z)$ are known at the poles $a_1, a_2, \ldots$ then provided that $f(z)$ behaves suitably on a contour $C_n$ which encloses the poles $a_1, a_2, \ldots, a_n$, we can find the expansion of $f(z)$ in a series of the above form. The function $f(z) = \operatorname{cosec} z - 1/z$ is an example† of this where

$$f(z) = \sum_{n=-\infty}^{\infty}{}' \; (-1)^n \left( \frac{1}{z-n\pi} + \frac{1}{n\pi} \right).$$

Another example is provided by Weierstrass's zeta function‡ $\zeta(u)$, in which there is a double summation.

### 7.4 Weierstrass's Theorem

This theorem is similar to the preceding. It concerns the construction of an integral function with simple zeros at $a_1, a_2, a_3, \ldots$ Let $w_r(z)$ be defined as before in Mittag–Leffler's theorem. $\sum\limits_{p+1}^{\infty} w_r(z)$ is absolutely and uniformly convergent in the circle $|z| = R$, where $R < |a_{p+1}|$. On integration we get

$$W_r(z) = \int_0^z w_r(z)\,dz = \left\{ \log\left(1-\frac{z}{a_r}\right) + \frac{z}{a_r} + \frac{1}{2}\frac{z^2}{a_r^2} + \ldots + \frac{1}{n-1}\frac{z^{n-1}}{a_r^{n-1}} \right\}$$

$$(r = p+1, \, p+2, \ldots)$$

where the path of integration lies in the circle.

Since the function $\sum\limits_{p+1}^{\infty} W_r(z)$ is regular in that region, so is

$$\prod_{p+1}^{\infty} \exp(W_r(z)).$$

Hence

$$\prod_{1}^{\infty} \left(1-\frac{z}{a_r}\right) \exp \phi(z), \tag{1}$$

† See *P.C.V.*, p. 132 for further details.
‡ See § 1.3.

where

$$\phi(z) = \frac{z}{a_r} + \frac{1}{2}\frac{z}{a_r^2} + \ldots + \frac{1}{n-1}\frac{z^{n-1}}{a_r^{n-1}},$$

is regular in the circle and has simple zeros at the points $a_1, a_2, \ldots,$ $a_p$. $R$ can be chosen so large that the circle includes any assigned point, so the theorem holds for all finite points.

We have already considered functions of the type (1) as Weierstrass's primary factors† in connection with the factorization of an integral function.

Weierstrass's sigma function‡ $\sigma(u)$ is an example of the type of function concerned above, $\sigma(u)/u$ being a (repeated) product of the above type (1). Also we have the sine product as another example:

$$\frac{\sin z}{z} = \prod_{-\infty}^{\infty}{}' \left(1 - \frac{z}{n\pi}\right)\exp\frac{z}{n\pi} = \prod_{1}^{\infty}\left(1 - \frac{z^2}{n^2\pi^2}\right).$$

### 7.5 Summation of Series by the Calculus of Residues

We have already considered some examples of this‖. The principle underlying the method depends on considering

$$\int F(z)\,\mathrm{d}z$$

round a suitable set of contours, such as the squares with vertices $\pm N \pm Ni$. If the integrals tend to zero as $N \to \infty$ then the sum of the residues of $F(z)$ at all its poles is zero. In this way various summations can be obtained. Take as an example

$$\frac{1}{2\pi i}\int_C f(z^4)\frac{\mathrm{d}z}{z}$$

round a square with vertices $\pm N \pm Ni$ where $f$ is a regular function. If $\varepsilon$ denotes any one of the fourth roots of unity and $a$ is a pole of the integrand so is $a\varepsilon$, and the residues at the four points $a\varepsilon$ are equal.

(1) Let

$$f(z^4) = \frac{\mathrm{cosec}\,\pi z\,\mathrm{cosech}\,\pi z}{z^2}, \tag{1}$$

---

† See § 6.2.
‡ See § 1.3.
‖ See *P.C.V.*, § 50.

and $N = n + \frac{1}{2}$, where $n$ is an integer. The poles of $f(z^4)/z$ are at 0 and $n\varepsilon$ $(n = 1, 2, 3, \ldots)$ and minus the residue at $n\varepsilon$ is

$$(-1)^{n-1} \frac{\text{cosech } n\pi}{\pi n^3}.$$

Hence

$$\frac{4}{\pi} \sum_{n=1}^{\infty} (-1)^{n-1} \frac{\text{cosech } n\pi}{n^3}$$

is equal to the residue of the integrand at the origin. The expansions of cosec $\pi z$ and cosech $\pi z$ involve Bernoulli's numbers†. The first few terms in the expansion of cosec $\pi x$ are

$$\frac{1}{\pi x} \left\{ 1 + \frac{1}{6}(\pi x)^2 + \frac{7}{360}(\pi x)^4 + \ldots \right\}$$

and that for cosech $\pi x$ is the same with alternating signs. Hence

$$\frac{\text{cosec } \pi z \text{ cosech } \pi z}{z^3} = \frac{1}{\pi^2 z^5} \left\{ 1 + \frac{1}{6}(\pi z)^2 + \frac{7}{360}(\pi z)^4 + \ldots \right\}$$

$$\times \left\{ 1 - \frac{1}{6}(\pi z)^2 + \ldots \right\}$$

and the residue at $z = 0$ is therefore the coefficient of $z^4$ in the product of the two series, i.e.

$$\frac{1}{\pi^2} \left\{ \frac{2.7}{360} - \frac{1}{36} \right\} \pi^4 = \frac{\pi^2}{90}.$$

Hence

$$\frac{\text{cosech } \pi}{1^3} - \frac{\text{cosech } 2\pi}{2^3} + \frac{\text{cosech } 3\pi}{3^3} - \ldots = \frac{\pi^3}{360}.$$

For the general result when the denominator in (1) is $z^{4m-2}$ see my Note on Summation of Series.‡ The above is the case when $m = 1$.

(2) By taking $f(z^4)$ as tanh $\pi z$ tan $\pi z / z^{4m+2}$, with $N = n$, we can use a similar method to show that, on taking $m = 1$,

$$\frac{\tanh(\pi/2)}{1^7} + \frac{\tanh(3\pi/2)}{2^7} + \frac{\tanh(5\pi/2)}{3^7} + \ldots = \frac{7\pi^7}{23{,}040}.$$

This is left as an exercise for the reader.

† See *P.A.*, p. 352 (5).
‡ E. G. Phillips, *J. London Math. Soc.* (1929), p. 114.

The above method was used by G. N. Watson[†] for summing some series stated by Ramanujan in his Notebooks. One such series,

$$\frac{\operatorname{sech}(\pi/2)}{1^5} - \frac{\operatorname{sech}(3\pi/2)}{3^5} + \frac{\operatorname{sech}(5\pi/2)}{5^5} - \cdots = \frac{\pi^5}{768},$$

is set as an example at the end of this chapter.

### 7.6 On Some Meromorphic Functions

If $\phi(z)$ is a meromorphic function and we draw small circles of arbitrarily small radii round each of its poles, let $T$ be the region outside these small circles. Then for a number of functions $\phi(z)$, $|\phi(z)| < M$, where $M$ is a constant, at every point of $T$. Among functions $\phi(z)$ satisfying this are

$$\sec z, \operatorname{cosec} z, \tan z, \cot z; \; \mathrm{e}^{xz}/(\mathrm{e}^z - 1), \mathrm{e}^{xz}/(\mathrm{e}^z + 1) \; (0 \leqslant x \leqslant 1).$$

Consider $\phi(z) = 1/(\mathrm{e}^z - 1)$. If $a$ is positive and $z = \lambda + i\mu$

$$|\phi(z)| < \frac{1}{\mathrm{e}^a - 1} \quad \text{if} \quad \lambda > a,$$

$$< \frac{1}{1 - \mathrm{e}^{-a}} \quad \text{if} \quad \lambda < -a,$$

and because of the periodicity of $\phi(z)$, $|\phi(z)|$ is bounded in the part of $T$ in the strip $-a \leqslant \lambda \leqslant a$. Let $M$ be the greatest of these three upper bounds.

Now consider

$$\psi(z) = \frac{\mathrm{e}^{xz}}{\mathrm{e}^z - 1} \quad (0 \leqslant x \leqslant 1).$$

We can write $\psi(z) = \exp\{-z(1-x)\}/\{1 - \mathrm{e}^{-z}\}$ and show similarly that $|\psi(z)| < M'$, where $M' = \mathrm{e}^a M$.

Similar proofs apply to the other functions listed above.

We shall use the notation $\mathscr{S}_C[f(z)]$ to denote the sum of the residues of $f(z)$ inside a given contour $C$. $\mathscr{S}_C \phi(z)[f(z)]$ will denote the sum of the residues of $\phi(z)f(z)$ at the poles of $f(z)$ inside $C$. The contours $C$ will generally be circles.

[†] J. London Math. Soc. (1928), p. 216.

Let $f(z)$ be meromorphic and consider a sequence of circles $C_1, C_2, \ldots, C_n, \ldots$ which do not pass through any of the poles. Let the radii of the circles be $r_1, r_2, \ldots, r_n, \ldots$ and put $z_n = r_n e^{i\theta}$.

$$\mathscr{S}_{C_n}[f(z)] = \frac{1}{2\pi i} \int_{C_n} f(z)\,\mathrm{d}z = \frac{1}{2\pi} \int_0^{2\pi} z_n f(z_n)\,\mathrm{d}\theta.$$

If this expression tends to a finite limit as $n \to \infty$, this limit is called the *complete residue* of $f(z)$ relative to the sequence $C_1, C_2, \ldots$ We denote the complete residue by $\mathscr{S}[f(z)]$. It follows from the definition that

$$\mathscr{S}[f(z)] = \mathscr{S}_{C_1} + (\mathscr{S}_{C_2} - \mathscr{S}_{C_1}) + (\mathscr{S}_{C_3} - \mathscr{S}_{C_2}) + \ldots \tag{1}$$

(I) *Suppose that* $\lim_{n \to \infty} z_n f(z_n) = A$ *is satisfied uniformly for* $0 \leqslant \theta \leqslant 2\pi$. *Then* $\mathscr{S}[f(z)] = A$.

For

$$\mathscr{S}_{C_n}[f(z)] - A = \frac{1}{2\pi} \int_0^{2\pi} \{z_n f(z_n) - A\}\,\mathrm{d}\theta, \tag{2}$$

and since $|z_n f(z_n) - A| < \varepsilon$ for $n > n_0$ the result follows.

(II) *More generally, the theorem holds if*

(i) $|z_n f(z_n)| < M$ *for every* $n$,

(ii) $\lim_{n \to \infty} z_n f(z_n) = A$ *uniformly in every part of the interval*

$0 \leqslant \theta \leqslant 2\pi$ *which does not include certain special values* $\theta_1, \theta_2, \ldots, \theta_n$.

For, if $\varepsilon$ and $\eta$ are arbitrary, and if we exclude from $0 \leqslant \theta \leqslant 2\pi$ the segments

$$\theta_k - \eta < \theta < \theta_k + \eta \qquad (k = 1, 2, \ldots, p)$$

whose total length does not exceed $2p\eta$, then the modulus of the left-hand side of (2) is less than $\varepsilon + 2p\eta(M + |A|)/2\pi$ for $n > n_0$ and so tends to zero as $n \to \infty$.

(III) *If instead of condition* (ii) *we have*

$$\lim_{n \to \infty} z_n f(z_n) = A \quad \text{when} \quad \theta_0 + \varepsilon < \theta < \theta_0 + \pi - \varepsilon$$
$$= B \quad \text{when} \quad \theta_0 + \pi + \varepsilon < \theta < \theta_0 + 2\pi - \varepsilon$$

*then similarly*

$$\mathscr{S}[f(z)] = \tfrac{1}{2}(A + B).$$

Suppose now we can choose the circles $C_n$ so that the conditions of (II) are satisfied when $f(z_n)$ replaces $z_n f(z_n)$, then we shall have, whatever $x$,

$$\lim_{n \to \infty} \frac{z_n f(z_n)}{z_n - x} = A,$$

and so

$$\mathscr{S} \left[ \frac{f(z)}{z - x} \right] = A.$$

But the residue of $f(z)/(z-x)$ at $z = x$ is $f(x)$ and so

$$f(x) = A + \mathscr{S} \frac{[f(z)]}{x - z} \tag{3}$$

Similarly if $f(z_n)$ replaces $z_n f(z_n)$ in the conditions of (III) we have

$$f(x) = \tfrac{1}{2}(A + B) + \mathscr{S} \frac{[f(z)]}{x - z}. \tag{4}$$

The formulae (3) and (4) can be used to express meromorphic functions in infinite series of rational fractions.

Let $f(z)$ be an *odd* function such that $f(z_n)/z_n \to 0$ uniformly for $0 \leqslant \theta \leqslant 2\pi$ as $n \to \infty$; then

$$\mathscr{S} \left[ \frac{f(z)}{z - x} \right] = 0$$

and we can apply (3) with $A = 0$, for

$$\mathscr{S}_{C_n} \left[ \frac{f(z)}{z - x} \right] = \frac{1}{2\pi} \int_0^{2\pi} \frac{z_n f(z_n)}{z_n - x} \, d\theta = \frac{x}{\pi} \int_0^{\pi} \frac{z_n f(z_n)}{z_n^2 - x^2} \, d\theta,$$

and the last term tends to 0 as $n \to \infty$.

If $f(z)$ has simple poles at $a_1, a_2, \ldots, a_n, \ldots$ then

$$\mathscr{S} \frac{[f(z)]}{x - z} = \sum_1^{\infty} \frac{A_n}{x - a_n},$$

where $A_n$ is the residue of $f(z)$ at $a_n$. But in this series we must collect the terms in groups, including in the same group the terms arising from the poles between pairs of consecutive circles $C_1, C_2, \ldots, C_n, \ldots$, as indicated in (1) above.

EXAMPLE 1. Let $\quad f(z) = \pi \cot \pi z = \dfrac{\sin' \pi z}{\sin \pi z}.$

$\sin \pi z$ has simple zeros at $0, \pm 1, \pm 2, \ldots$ so $f(z)$ has simple poles at these points with residue 1. $f(z)$ is odd and $|f(z)|$ is bounded on the circles $C_n$ if $r_n = n - \frac{1}{2}$. Applying (3) with $A = 0$ we get

$$\pi \cot \pi x = \frac{1}{x} + \sum_{n=1}^{\infty} \left( \frac{1}{x-n} + \frac{1}{x+n} \right) = \frac{1}{x} + 2x \sum_{1}^{\infty} \frac{1}{x^2 - n^2}.$$

EXAMPLE 2. Let $f(z) = \dfrac{e^{az}}{e^z - 1}$ $(0 < a < 1)$.

Take $r_n = (2n-1)\pi$. $|f(z)| < M$ on the circles $C_n$, as was shown earlier, and $\lim_{n \to \infty} f(z_n) = 0$ is satisfied uniformly for

$$-\tfrac{1}{2}\pi + \varepsilon < \theta < \tfrac{1}{2}\pi - \varepsilon \quad \text{and} \quad \tfrac{1}{2}\pi + \varepsilon < \theta < \frac{3\pi}{2} - \varepsilon.$$

Hence from (3) with $A = 0$ we have

$$\frac{e^{ax}}{e^x - 1} = \lim_{m \to \infty} \sum_{-m}^{m} \frac{\exp(2\pi i n a)}{x - 2n\pi i} \quad (0 < a < 1).$$

If $a = 0$ we have

$$\lim_{n \to \infty} f(z_n) = -1 \quad \text{for} \quad \tfrac{1}{2}\pi + \varepsilon < \theta < \frac{3\pi}{2} - \varepsilon,$$

the other conditions being the same as above.

Hence we can apply (4) with $A = 0$, $B = 1$ and obtain the result

$$\frac{1}{e^x - 1} = -\frac{1}{2} + \frac{1}{x} + 2x \sum_{1}^{\infty} \frac{1}{x^2 + 4n^2\pi^2}.$$

### 7.7 Some Further Summations

We have already considered†

$$\int_C \pi \cot \pi z f(z) \, dz \quad \text{and} \quad \int_C \pi \operatorname{cosec} \pi z f(z) \, dz$$

and used them to determine some infinite series expansions of $f(z)$ when $f(z)$ is such that the contour integrals tend to zero as $n \to \infty$. In this treatment the contours $C_n$ were squares but it

† *P.C.V.*, § 50.

applies equally when they are circles. The results there obtained can be expressed in terms of complete residues:

$$\sum_{-\infty}^{\infty} f(n) = -\mathscr{S} \, \pi \cot \pi z [f(z)], \tag{1}$$

$$\sum_{-\infty}^{\infty} (-1)^n f(n) = -\mathscr{S} \pi \operatorname{cosec} \pi z [f(z)]. \tag{2}$$

Write $f(z) = \phi(z) \sin az$, where $\phi(z)$ is a rational function which tends to zero at infinity and $-\pi < a < \pi$. By replacing the trigonometrical functions by exponentials we can show that $g(z) = |\sin az \operatorname{cosec} \pi z|$ is bounded on the circles $|z| = n - \frac{1}{2}$ $(n = 1, 2, \ldots)$ and that $g(z)$ tends uniformly to zero when $z = \rho e^{i\psi}$ tends to infinity within one of the angles $\varepsilon < \psi < \pi - \varepsilon$, $\pi + \varepsilon < \psi < 2\pi - \varepsilon$. Since $|z\phi(z)|$ is bounded, the same is true of $\pi z \operatorname{cosec} \pi z \phi(z) \sin az$. By the previous section, the complete residues of these functions reduce to zero and so, under the conditions stated

$$\sum_{1}^{\infty} (-1)^n \{\phi(n) - \phi(-n)\} \sin na = -\pi \mathscr{S} \sin az \operatorname{cosec} \pi z [\phi(z)].$$

If $\phi(z) = 1/(x - z)$ we get

$$\sum_{1}^{\infty} (-1)^n \frac{n \sin na}{x^2 - n^2} = \frac{\pi}{2} \frac{\sin ax}{\sin \pi x}.$$

If we take $f(z) = \phi(z) \cos az$ we obtain a similar result when $\phi(z) = 1/(x - z)$,

$$\sum_{1}^{\infty} (-1)^n \frac{\cos na}{x^2 - n^2} = -\frac{1}{2x^2} + \frac{\pi \cos ax}{2x \sin \pi x}.$$

For further results of this kind the reader is referred elsewhere.†

## Examples 7

**1.** If in Lagrange's expansion (§ 7.1) $f(z) = \sin z$ show that the coefficient of $\lambda^n$ is

$$\sum_{r=0}^{\infty} \frac{(n - 2r)^{n-1}(-1)^r}{r!(n - r)!2^{n+1}} \sin(n - 2r)a.$$

† See Lindelöf, *Le Calcul des Résidus*, (Paris, 1905).

**2.** Use Lagrange's expansion to show that, if $b > 0$, $(1 - 2c\lambda + b\lambda^2)^{-\frac{1}{2}}$ can be expanded in the form

$$1 + \sum_{n=1}^{\infty} \frac{\lambda^n}{n!} \frac{d^n}{da^n} \left\{ \frac{(a-p)(a-q)}{2} \right\}^n,$$

where $a$ is arbitrary and $p = a - c + \sqrt{b}$, $q = a - c - \sqrt{b}$.
Deduce that, when $b = 1$, the expansion is

$$1 + \sum_{1}^{\infty} \lambda^n P_n(\lambda),$$

where $P_n(\lambda)$ is Legendre's polynomial of degree $n$.

**3.** If $ze^{az} = w$ show that

$$e^{kz} = 1 + kw + \frac{k(k-2a)}{2!} w^2 + \frac{k(k-3a)}{3!} w^3 + \cdots$$

provided that $|w| < 1/(e|a|)$.

**4.** Prove that

$$\sec \pi x = \frac{4}{\pi} \left\{ \frac{1}{1^2 - 4x^2} - \frac{3}{3^2 - 4x^2} + \frac{5}{5^2 - 4x^2} - \cdots \right\}.$$

**5.** Prove that

$$\frac{\cosh \pi - \cos \pi x}{1 - \cos \pi x} = \left\{ 1 + \frac{1}{x^2} \right\} \left\{ 1 + \frac{1}{(2-x)^2} \right\} \left\{ 1 + \frac{1}{(2+x)^2} \right\} \left\{ 1 + \frac{1}{(4-x)^2} \right\} \left\{ 1 + \frac{1}{(4+x)^2} \right\} \cdots$$

**6.** Use the method of § 7.5 to prove that

(i) $\quad \dfrac{\mathrm{sech}(\pi/2)}{1^5} - \dfrac{\mathrm{sech}(3\pi/2)}{3^5} + \dfrac{\mathrm{sech}(5\pi/2)}{5^5} - \cdots = \dfrac{\pi^5}{768}$;

(ii) $\quad \dfrac{\coth \pi}{1^7} + \dfrac{\coth 2\pi}{2^7} + \dfrac{\coth 3\pi}{3^7} + \cdots = \dfrac{19\pi^7}{56{,}700}$;

(iii) $\quad \displaystyle\sum_{n=0}^{\infty} (-1)^n \frac{\mathrm{sech}(n + \frac{1}{2})\pi}{(2n+1)\{(2n+1)^4 + 4\}} = \frac{1}{32} \left\{ 1 - \frac{2}{\coth \pi - 1} \right\}.$

$$\left[ \text{For (iii) take } f(z^4) = \frac{\mathrm{sech}\, \pi z \sec \pi z}{z^4 + \frac{1}{4}}. \right]$$

**7.** Using the usual contour for many-valued functions (*P.C.V.*, p. 126) and taking $\phi(z)$ rational, regular at $z = 0$ and on the positive real axis, and $\phi(z) \to 0$ as $|z| \to \infty$, show that, if $0 < a < 1$,

$$\int_0^{\infty} z^{a-1} \phi(z) \, dz = \frac{2\pi i}{1 - \exp(2\pi i a)} \mathscr{S} z^{a-1} [\phi(z)].$$

By differentiating $n$ times with respect to $a$ show that, for suitable $\phi(z)$, if $a = 1 + \varepsilon$, $0 < \varepsilon < 1$,

$$\int_0^{\infty} \phi(z)(\log z)^n \, dz = \lim_{\varepsilon \to 0} D_\varepsilon^{(n)} \left\{ \frac{2\pi i}{1 - \exp(2\pi i \varepsilon)} \mathscr{S} z^{\varepsilon} [\phi(z)] \right\}.$$

Deduce that

$$\int_0^\infty \frac{(\log z)^2}{1+z^2}\, dz = \frac{\pi^3}{8}.$$

**8.** Show that

(i) $\displaystyle\sum_{-\infty}^{\infty} \frac{1}{(x+n)^2} = \frac{\pi^2}{\sin^2 \pi x},$

(ii) $\displaystyle\sum_1^{\infty} \frac{1}{a^2+b^2n^2} = -\frac{1}{2a^2} + \frac{\pi}{2ab}\coth\frac{\pi a}{b}.$

[Use eqn. (1) of §7.7.]

**9.** If

$$f(z) = \frac{1}{z^p}\frac{e^{tz}}{e^z - 1} \quad (0 < t < 1),$$

show that if $p > 1$ the complete residue of $f(z)$ is 0, where $r_n = (2n-1)\pi$ (see §7.6(II)). If

$$\frac{e^{tz}}{e^z - 1} = \frac{1}{z} + \sum_{n=1}^{\infty} \frac{g_n(t)z^{n-1}}{n!} \quad (0 < t < 1),$$

show that

$$g_{2k}(t) = (-1)^{k+1}2(2k)! \sum_{n=1}^{\infty} \frac{\cos 2n\pi t}{(2n\pi)^{2k}},$$

$$g_{2k+1}(t) = (-1)^{k+1}2(2k+1)! \sum_{n=1}^{\infty} \frac{\sin 2n\pi t}{(2n\pi)^{2k+1}}.$$

**10.** By integrating $\sin^p(\theta z).z^{-p} \operatorname{cosec} \pi z$, where $\theta$ is real and $p$ is a positive integer, round the circle $|z| = R$, prove that if $0 < \theta < \pi/p$

$$\sum_{n=1}^{\infty} (-1)^{n-1}\frac{\sin^p n\theta}{n^p} = \tfrac{1}{2}\theta^p.$$

**11.** If $a$ and $b$ are real and $-\pi < b < \pi$, show that

$$\int_0^\infty \frac{1}{\cos b + \cosh x}\frac{dx}{a^2+x^2} = \frac{2\pi b}{a \sin b}\sum_{n=0}^{\infty} \frac{1}{\{(2n+1)\pi+a\}^2 - b^2}.$$

(Integrate a function of the type $[e^{az}/(1+2pe^z \pm e^{2z})(z+ia)]$ round a square of corners $\pm N$, $\pm N+2Ni$ and make $N \to \infty$.)

**12.** Using the same contour as suggested in 11 prove that

$$\int_0^\infty \frac{dt}{(1+t^2)\cosh \tfrac{1}{2}\pi nt} = 2\left(\frac{1}{n+1} - \frac{1}{n+3} + \frac{1}{n+5} - \ldots\right).$$

**13.** By integrating a suitable function round a suitably indented rectangle, or otherwise, prove that

$$\int_0^\infty \frac{dx}{\sqrt{x}\cosh \pi x} = 2\sum_{m=0}^{\infty} \frac{(-1)^m}{\sqrt{(2m+1)}}.$$

## CHAPTER 8

# CONTOUR INTEGRALS DEFINING SOME SPECIAL FUNCTIONS

## 8.1 Definition of Regular Functions by Integrals

THEOREM A. *Let $f(z, w)$ be a continuous function of the two complex variables $z$, $w$ where $z$ ranges over a region $D$ and $w$ lies on a contour $C$. If $f(z, w)$ is a regular function of $z$ in $D$ for every value of $w$ on $C$, then*

$$F(z) = \int_C f(z, w) \, dw$$

*is a regular function of $z$ in $D$ and its successive derivatives can be found by differentiation with respect to $z$ under the integral sign.*

The theorem can be extended to infinite integrals.

THEOREM A1. *If $C$ is a contour going to infinity any bounded part of which is regular, if the conditions of Theorem A are satisfied on any bounded part of $C$ and if*

$$\int_C f(z, w) \, dw$$

*is uniformly convergent with respect to $z$, then the results of Theorem A still hold.*

THEOREM A2. *If there is a finite contour $C$ at one end of which $f(z, w) \to \infty$ then*

$$\int_C f(z, w) \, dw$$

*is a regular function of $z$ provided that the convergence of the integral is uniform.*

Proofs of Theorems A and A1 are given in Titchmarsh, *Theory of Functions*, § 2.83 *et seq.* They are all extensions of well-known

120

theorems on infinite integrals with a real parameter to integrals of functions with a complex parameter.

EXAMPLE. If $z$ is real and positive,

$$\int_0^\infty e^{-zt}\,dt = \frac{1}{z}. \tag{1}$$

This integral is uniformly convergent in any finite region to the right of the imaginary axis and so represents a regular function of $z$ for $\mathscr{R}z > 0$. Hence

$$F(z) = \int_0^\infty e^{-zt}\,dt - \frac{1}{z}$$

is regular for $\mathscr{R}z > 0$ and $F(z) = 0$ on the real axis. Hence $F(z) = 0$ whenever it is regular, so that (1) holds for complex values of $z = x + iy$ when $x > 0$.

## 8.2  Analytic Continuation by Means of an Integral

The method of analytic continuation by means of power series has already been considered.† This leads to the Weierstrassian definition of an analytic function. But for some purposes the method of continuation by power series is not the most convenient. An example of this is the Gamma function. The formula

$$\Gamma(z) = \int_0^\infty e^{-t}t^{z-1}\,dt \tag{1}$$

is one definition of the function $\Gamma(z)$ for $\mathscr{R}z > 0$. It is easily shown that when $z$ is real ($z = x$) the integral always converges at the upper limit and also at the lower limit if $x > 0$.‡ If $z$ is complex, the integral is uniformly convergent over any finite region throughout which $\mathscr{R}z \geqslant a > 0$, for $|t^{z-1}| = t^{x-1}$ and the result then follows from the real case. The formula (1) tells us nothing about $\Gamma(z)$ when $\mathscr{R}z \leqslant 0$. The difficulty at $z = 0$ is the divergence of the integral (1). To avoid this, we discuss Hankel's contour integral

$$f(z) = \int_C (-t)^{z-1}e^{-t}\,dt, \tag{2}$$

† P.C.V., p. 103–7.
‡ See P.A., p. 197.

9

where $C$ is the contour of Fig. 16, with its initial and final points at infinity on the real axis of $t$.

The many-valued function $(-t)^{z-1} = \exp\{(z-1)\log(-t)\}$ is made definite by taking $\log(-t)$ to be real at a point where $t$ is real and negative.

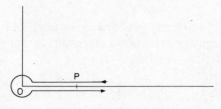

FIG. 16.

The integral (2) is uniformly convergent for any finite region of the $z$-plane, for the question of convergence now arises at infinity only; there, if $\mathscr{R}z \leqslant k$, uniform convergence follows by comparison with

$$\int\limits_{0}^{\infty} e^{-t}t^{k-1}\,dt,$$

and so $f(z)$ is required for all finite values of $z$. The restriction $\mathscr{R}z > 0$ is no longer required. The function $f(z)$ is thus continued across the imaginary axis.

## 8.3 The Gamma Function

Let $P$ be the point $t = p$ on the real axis and let the contour of Fig. 16 now start and finish at $P$. Let $\mathscr{R}z > 0$ and $z$ be not an integer.

$$f(z) = \int\limits_{C} (-t)^{z-1}e^{-t}\,dt$$

involves the many-valued function $(-t)^{z-1}$. We make this definite by the convention that $(-t)^{z-1} = \exp\{(z-1)\log(-t)\}$ and $\log(-t)$ is real when $t$ is on the negative part of the real axis, so that on $C$, $-\pi \leqslant \arg(-t) \leqslant \pi$. Along the upper edge of the cut, $\arg(-t) = -\pi$ so that $(-t)^{z-1} = \exp\{-i\pi(z-1)\}t^{z-1}$ and on the lower edge

$(-t)^{z-1} = \exp\{i\pi(z-1)\}t^{z-1}$. On the small circle $-t = \delta e^{i\theta}$. Then

$$\int_C (-t)^{z-1} e^{-t}\,dt = \int_p^{\delta} \exp\{-i\pi(z-1)\}t^{z-1}e^{-t}\,dt$$

$$+ \int_{-\pi}^{\pi} (\delta e^{i\theta})^{z-1} \exp\{\delta e^{i\theta}\}\delta e^{i\theta} i\,d\theta$$

$$+ \int_{\delta}^{p} \exp\{i\pi(z-1)\}t^{z-1}e^{-t}\,dt,$$

$$= -2i\sin\pi z \int_{\delta}^{p} t^{z-1}e^{-t}\,dt + i\delta^z \int_{-\pi}^{\pi} \exp\{zi\theta + \delta e^{i\theta}\}\,d\theta.$$

This is true for all positive $\delta \leqslant p$. Make $\delta \to 0$; then $\delta^z \to 0$ and

$$\int_{-\pi}^{\pi} \exp\{zi\theta + \delta e^{i\theta}\}\,d\theta \to \int_{-\pi}^{\pi} e^{zi\theta}\,d\theta$$

uniformly.  It follows that

$$\int_C (-t)^{z-1} e^{-t}\,dt = -2i\sin\pi z \int_0^{p} t^{z-1}e^{-t}\,dt,$$

and this is true for all positive $p$.  Make $p \to \infty$; then

$$\int_C (-t)^{z-1} e^{-t}\,dt = -2i\sin\pi z \int_0^{\infty} e^{-t}t^{z-1}\,dt. \tag{1}$$

Since the contour $C$ does not pass through $t = 0$, we need no longer stipulate that $\mathscr{R}z > 0$ and the left-hand side of (1) is a regular function of $z$ for all $z$.  It follows by analytic continuation that (1) holds for all $z$ except $z = 0, \pm 1, \pm 2, \dots$ Since we know that $\Gamma(z)$ is regular at $z = 1, 2, \dots$ the only possible poles of $\Gamma(z)$ are $z = 0, -1, -2, \dots$ The points $z = 0, -1, -2, \dots$ are poles of $\Gamma(z)$.  For, if $n$ is a positive integer,

$$f(-n) = \int_C e^{-t}(-t)^{-n-1}\,dt.$$

Since $(-t)^{-n-1}$ is one-valued, the integral is $2\pi i$ times the residue at the origin and this is $-1/n!$  Hence $f(-n) = -2\pi i/n!$

Hence the residue of $\Gamma(z)$ at $z = -n$ is.

$$\lim_{z \to -n} \frac{2\pi i}{n!} \frac{z+n}{2i \sin \pi z} = \frac{(-1)^n}{n!}.$$

We have shown that, for all except integer values of $z$,

$$\Gamma(z) = \frac{i}{2 \sin \pi z} \int_C (-t)^{z-1} e^{-t} dt. \tag{2}$$

By writing $1-z$ for $z$ and using the known result

$$\Gamma(z)\Gamma(1-z) = \pi \operatorname{cosec} \pi z,$$

$$\frac{1}{\Gamma(z)} = \frac{i}{2\pi} \int_C (-t)^z e^{-t} dt, \tag{3}$$

from which we see that $1/\Gamma(z)$ is an integral function.

We could, of course, have taken the cut along the negative real axis.  If we do this, (2) and (3) become

$$\Gamma(z) = \frac{1}{2i \sin \pi z} \int_{C'} e^t t^{z-1} dt, \tag{2'}$$

$$\frac{1}{\Gamma(z)} = \frac{1}{2\pi i} \int_{C'} e^t t^{-z} dt, \tag{3'}$$

where $C'$ is now the contour consisting of the cut from $-\infty$ to $0$ and the small circle around the origin.  $C$ and $C'$ are sometimes written

$$\int_{\infty}^{0+} \quad \text{and} \quad \int_{-\infty}^{0+}$$

respectively.

## 8.4 The Riemann Zeta function

Let $s = \sigma + it$; then if $\delta > 0$ the series

$$\zeta(s) = \sum_{n=1}^{\infty} \frac{1}{n^s}$$

is $n$ uniformly convergent series of regular functions in any domain $D$ in which $\sigma \geqslant 1 + \delta$ and so the series is a regular function of $s$ in $D$. More generally

$$\zeta(s, a) = \sum_{n=0}^{\infty} \frac{1}{(a+n)^s}$$

defines a function, if $\sigma \geqslant 1 + \delta$, $0 < a \leqslant 1$, $\arg(a+n) = 0$, which reduces to $\zeta(s)$ if $a = 1$. We show that $\zeta(s, a)$ can be expressed as an infinite integral. Since

$$(a+n)^{-s}\Gamma(s) = \int_{0}^{\infty} x^{s-1} e^{-(n+a)x} dx,$$

when $\arg x = 0$ and $\sigma > 0$, we have, if $\sigma \geqslant 1 + \delta$,

$$\Gamma(s)\zeta(s, a) = \lim_{N \to \infty} \sum_{n=0}^{N} \int_{0}^{\infty} x^{s-1} e^{-(n+a)x} dx$$

$$= \lim_{N \to \infty} \left\{ \int_{0}^{\infty} \frac{x^{s-1} e^{-ax}}{1 - e^{-x}} dx - \int_{0}^{\infty} \frac{x^{s-1}}{1 - e^{-x}} e^{-(N+1+a)x} dx \right\}.$$

If $x \geqslant 0$, $e^x \geqslant 1 + x$, and so the modulus of the second integral does not exceed

$$\int_{0}^{\infty} x^{\sigma-2} e^{-(N+a)x} dx = (N+a)^{1-\sigma}\Gamma(\sigma-1)$$

which, when $\sigma \geqslant 1 + \delta$, tends to zero as $N \to \infty$.

Hence, when $\sigma \geqslant 1 + \delta$ and $\arg x = 0$,

$$\zeta(s, a) = \frac{1}{\Gamma(s)} \int_{0}^{\infty} \frac{x^{s-1} e^{-ax}}{1 - e^{-x}} dx,$$

an integral which somewhat resembles Euler's definition of the gamma function.

## 8.5 A Contour Integral for $\zeta(s, a)$

If $\sigma \geqslant 1 + \delta$ consider an integral with a contour of Hankel's type (§ 8.2, Fig. 16)

$$\int\limits_{\infty}^{0+} \frac{(-z)^{s-1} e^{-az}}{1 - e^{-z}} \, dz$$

The contour does not contain any of the poles of the integrand $\pm 2n\pi i (n = 1, 2, \ldots)$ and we suppose, as in § 8.2, that $|\arg(-z)| \leqslant \pi$. If $\sigma \geqslant 1 + \delta$,

$$\int\limits_{\infty}^{0+} \frac{(-z)^{s-1} e^{-az}}{1 - e^{-z}} \, dz = [\exp\{\pi i(s-1)\} - \exp\{-\pi i(s-1)\}]$$

$$\times \int\limits_{0}^{\infty} \frac{x^{s-1} e^{-ax}}{1 - e^{-x}} \, dx.$$

Hence

$$\zeta(s, a) = -\frac{\Gamma(1-s)}{2\pi i} \int\limits_{\infty}^{0+} \frac{(-z)^{s-1} e^{-az}}{1 - e^{-z}} \, dz. \tag{1}$$

The last integral is a regular function of $s$ for all values of $s$, and so the only possible singularities of $\zeta(s, a)$ are those of $\Gamma(1-s)$ which are at the points $1, 2, 3, \ldots$ With the exception of these points, the integral (1), of Hankel's type, represents $\zeta(s, a)$ over the whole plane.

Since $\zeta(s, a)$ is regular when $\sigma \geqslant 1 + \delta$ the only singularity of $\zeta(s, a)$ is at $s = 1$. Putting $s = 1$ in (1) we have

$$\frac{1}{2\pi i} \int\limits_{\infty}^{0+} \frac{e^{-az}}{1 - e^{-z}} \, dz,$$

and this is the residue at $z = 0$ of the integrand, which is readily seen to be 1. Hence

$$\lim_{s \to 1} \frac{\zeta(s, a)}{\Gamma(1-s)} = -1.$$

Since $\Gamma(1-s)$ has a single pole at $s = 1$ with residue $-1$, the only singularity of $\zeta(s, a)$ is a simple pole with residue 1 at $s = 1$.

## 8.6 The Legendre Function $P_n(z)$

If $z$ is real the Legendre polynomial $P_n(x)$ possesses a number of properties† and there are several possible definitions. For our present purpose we shall define $P_n(z)$ by Rodrigue's formula

$$P_n(z) = \frac{1}{2^n \cdot n!} \frac{d^n}{dz^n} (z^2 - 1)^n.$$

When $n$ is a positive integer, this is Legendre's polynomial of degree $n$. On using the definition above and the integral formula for $f^{(n)}(\zeta)$‡ we get Schläfli's integral formula for the Legendre polynomials

$$P_n(z) = \frac{1}{2\pi i} \int_C \frac{(t^2 - 1)^n}{2^n(t - z)^{n+1}} \, dt, \tag{1}$$

where $C$ is any simple contour encircling the point $z$ once anti-clockwise. The integral (1) satisfies

$$(1 - z^2)\frac{d^2 u}{dz^2} - 2z\frac{du}{dz} + n(n+1)u = 0,$$

for on substituting $u = P_n(z)$ in the left-hand side we get

$$\frac{n+1}{2\pi i} \int_C \frac{(t^2 - 1)^n \, dt}{2^n(t - z)^{n+3}} \left\{ -(n+2)(t^2 - 1) + 2(n+1)t(t - z) \right\}$$

$$= \frac{(n+1)}{2^n \cdot 2\pi i} \int_C \frac{d}{dt} \left\{ \frac{(t^2 - 1)^{n+1}}{(t - z)^{n+2}} \right\} dt$$

and this integral is zero, since $(t^2 - 1)^{n+1}(t - z)^{-n-2}$ resumes its original value after describing $C$ when $n$ is an integer.

To define the Legendre function $P_n(z)$, when $n$ is not a positive integer, we use (1), with the proviso that that

$$\phi(t) = (t^2 - 1)^{n+1}(t - z)^{-n-2}$$

resumes its original value after describing $C$. The function $\phi(t)$ has three branch points $t = \pm 1$, $t = z$. If $C$ goes round $t = 1$ once in the positive sense, $\phi(t)$ resumes its original value multiplied by

† See *P.A.*, pp. 198–205.
‡ *P.C.V.*, p. 95, V.

$\exp\{2(n+1)\pi i\}$. If $C$ goes similarly once round $t = z$, $\phi(z)$ resumes its original value multiplied by $\exp\{2\pi i(-n-2)\}$. Hence if $C$ is a contour including $t = 1$ and $t = z$ but excluding $t = -1$, $\phi(z)$ will resume its original value after describing $C$. We therefore define $P_n(z)$, the Legendre function of the first kind, whether $n$ is an integer or not, by

$$w = \frac{1}{2\pi i} \int_{a}^{1+,z+} \frac{(t^2-1)^n}{2^n(t-z)^{n+1}}\, dt,$$

the integrand being many-valued when $n$ is not an integer. We choose $a$ on the real axis to the right of $t = 1$, and if $z$ is real to the right of this point also. At $a$ we take $\arg(t-1) = \arg(t+1) = 0$ and $|\arg(t-z)| < \pi$. Notice that the function $w$ so defined is not a one-valued function of $z$, for we can choose two different contours, both including $t = 1$ and $t = z$ and excluding $t = -1$, and the integrals along these two contours would not necessarily be the same. To make the contour integral unique, it is necessary to cut the $t$-plane from $-\infty$ to $-1$ and a similar cut must be made in the $z$-plane.

## 8.7 The Bessel Function $J_n(z)$ when $n$ is an Integer

When $z$ is complex we start by expanding $\exp\{\frac{1}{2}z(t-t^{-1})\}$ by Laurent's theorem† in a series of positive and negative powers of $t$. This expansion is possible for all values of $z$ and $t$, except $t = 0$, and the coefficient of $t^n$, where $n$ is any integer, positive or negative, is

$$J_n(z) = \frac{1}{2\pi i} \int^{0+} u^{-n-1} \exp\{\tfrac{1}{2}z(u-u^{-1})\}\, du. \tag{1}$$

If we put $u = 2t|z$ we get

$$J_n(z) = \frac{1}{2\pi i}(\tfrac{1}{2}z)^n \int^{0+} t^{-n-1} \exp\left\{t-\frac{z^2}{4t}\right\} dt.$$

Since the contour is any one which encircles the origin once anti-clockwise, we may choose it to be the circle $|t| = 1$. If we expand

† P.C.V., p. 97.

the integrand in powers of $z$, the series is uniformly convergent on $|t| = 1$, hence

$$J_n(z) = \frac{1}{2\pi i} \sum_{r=0}^{\infty} \frac{(-1)^r}{r!} \left(\frac{z}{2}\right)^{n+2r} \int^{0+} t^{-n-r-1} e^t \, dt.$$

If $n+r$ is an integer the residue of the integrand at $t = 0$ is $\{(n+r)!\}^{-1}$ if $n+r \geqslant 0$, and zero if $n+r < 0$. Hence when $n$ is a positive integer or zero

$$J_n(z) = \sum_{r=0}^{\infty} \frac{(-1)^r (\tfrac{1}{2} z)^{n+2r}}{r!(n+r)!}. \tag{2}$$

To extend the definition to the case where $n$ is any number, real or complex we define $J_n(z)$ by

$$\frac{(\tfrac{1}{2} z)^n}{2\pi i} \int_{-\infty}^{0+} t^{-n-1} \exp\left(t - \frac{z^2}{4t}\right) dt, \tag{3}$$

where $\arg z$ has its principal value and $|\arg t| \leqslant \pi$ on the contour. Since the integrand is a regular function of $z$ we may obtain the coefficients in the Taylor expansion by differentiation under the integral signs; hence

$$J_n(z) = \frac{z^n}{2^{n+1}\pi i} \sum_0^{\infty} \frac{(-1)^r z^{2r}}{2^{2r} r!} \int_{-\infty}^{0+} e^{-t} t^{-n-r-1} \, dt$$

$$= \sum_{r=0}^{\infty} \frac{(-1)^r z^{n+2r}}{2^{n+2r} r! \Gamma(n+r+1)}.$$

This clearly reduces to (2) when $n$ is an integer.

### 8.8 Bessel's Integral when $n$ is not an Integer

If in the integral (1) we put $u = e^{i\theta}$ and take as contour the circle $|u| = 1$

$$J_n(z) = \frac{1}{2\pi} \int_{-\pi}^{\pi} \exp\{-ni\theta + iz \sin \theta\} \, d\theta.$$

If we bisect the range of integration and in the first half write $-\theta$

10

for $\theta$ we obtain

$$J_n(z) = \frac{1}{\pi} \int_0^\pi \cos(n\theta - z\sin\theta)\,d\theta$$

when $n$ is an integer.

When $n$ is not an integer we shall show that Schläfli's integral for $J_n(z)$ is

$$\frac{1}{\pi} \int_0^\pi \cos(n\theta - z\sin\theta)\,d\theta - \frac{\sin n\pi}{\pi} \int_0^\infty e^{-n\theta - z\sinh\theta}\,d\theta. \tag{1}$$

The second term is plainly zero if $n$ is an integer.

In the integral (3) of § 8.7 suppose that $z$ is positive and put $t = \tfrac{1}{2}uz$, then

$$J_n(z) = \frac{1}{2\pi i} \int_{-\infty}^{0+} u^{-n-1} \exp\{\tfrac{1}{2}z(u - u^{-1})\}\,du.$$

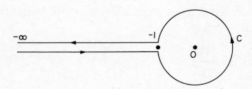

Fig. 17.

Let the contour be the real axis from $-\infty$ to $-1$ taken twice and the contour $C$ which is the circle $|u| = 1$. The integral is a regular function of $z$ when $R(zu) < 0$ as $|u| \to \infty$ on the path, i.e. when $|\arg z| < \tfrac{1}{2}\pi$, and by analytic continuation the formula proved for positive values of $z$ is true whenever $R(z) > 0$.

Hence

$$J_n(z) = \frac{1}{2\pi i} \left\{ \int_{-\infty}^{-1} + \int_C + \int_{-1}^{-\infty} \right\} u^{-n-1} \exp\{\tfrac{1}{2}z(u - u^{-1})\}\,du,$$

where $\arg u = -\pi$ on the first path and $+\pi$ on the third path.

Write $u = t\,e^{-\pi i}$ in the first, $u = t\,e^{\pi i}$ in the third and $u = e^{i\theta}$ in the second integral then

$$J_n(z) = \frac{1}{2\pi} \int_{-\pi}^{\pi} \exp\{-ni\theta + iz\sin\theta\}\,d\theta +$$

$$\frac{1}{2\pi i}[\exp\{(n+1)\pi i\}$$

$$- \exp\{-(n+1)\pi i\}]\int_{1}^{\infty} t^{-n-1}\exp\left\{\frac{1}{2}z\left(-t+\frac{1}{t}\right)\right\}\,dt.$$

The first of the two integrals can be modified as above and so

$$J_n(z) = \frac{1}{\pi}\int_{0}^{\pi} \cos(n\theta - z\sin\theta)\,d\theta$$

$$+\frac{\sin(n+1)\pi}{\pi}\int_{0}^{\infty} \exp\{-n\theta - z\sinh\theta\}\,d\theta,$$

where in the second integral $e^{\theta}$ has been written for $t$, and

$$|\arg z| < \tfrac{1}{2}\pi.$$

## 8.9 Hankel's Contour Integral for $J_n(z)$

Consider

$$u = z^n \int_{C} (t^2 - 1)^{n-\frac{1}{2}} \cos zt\,dt,$$

where $C$ is the contour of Fig. 18, $a$ being to the right of $t = 1$ and, at $a$, $\arg(t-1) = \arg(t+1) = 0$;

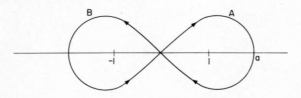

FIG. 18.

so that

$$\int_C = \int_a^{1+,-1-} \quad \text{in what follows.}$$

The integrand returns to its original value after $t$ has traversed $C$, for $(t-1)^{n-\frac{1}{2}}$ is multiplied by $\exp\{(2n-1)\pi i\}$ after loop $A$ has been traversed and $(t+1)^{n-\frac{1}{2}}$ by $\exp\{-(2n-1)\pi i\}$ after loop $B$ has been traversed. The series

$$\sum_{r=0}^{\infty} \frac{(-1)^r (zt)^{2r}}{(2r)!} (t^2-1)^{n-\frac{1}{2}}$$

is uniformly convergent on $C$ and so, by term-by-term integration,

$$u = \sum_{r=0}^{\infty} \frac{(-1)^r z^{n+2r}}{(2r)!} \int_C t^{2r}(t^2-1)^{n-\frac{1}{2}} \, dt.$$

If $R(n+\frac{1}{2}) > 0$ the integrals are regular functions of $n$, so we can deform $C$ into $\Gamma$ of Fig. 19, where the small circles have radii $\delta$.

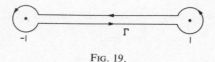

$$\text{FIG. 19.}$$

As $\delta \to 0$ the integrals round the small circles $\to 0$; and if $\arg(1-t^2) = 0$, $t^2 = v$ we get, on writing $\phi(t)$ for $t^{2r}(1-t^2)^{n-\frac{1}{2}}$, the integral in (1) becomes

$$\exp\{(n-\tfrac{1}{2})\pi i\} \int_1^{-1} \phi(t)\,dt + \exp\{-(n-\tfrac{1}{2})\pi i\} \int_{-1}^{1} \phi(t)\,dt$$

$$= -4i \sin(n-\tfrac{1}{2})\pi \int_0^1 \phi(t)\,dt$$

$$= -2i \sin(n-\tfrac{1}{2})\pi \int_0^1 v^{r-\frac{1}{2}}(1-v)^{n-\frac{1}{2}}\,dv$$

$$= 2i \sin(n+\tfrac{1}{2})\pi \Gamma(n+\tfrac{1}{2})\Gamma(r+\tfrac{1}{2})/\Gamma(n+r+1).$$

Hence

$$u = \sum_{r=0}^{\infty} \frac{(-1)^r z^{n+2r} 2i \sin(n+\tfrac{1}{2})\pi \Gamma(n+\tfrac{1}{2})\Gamma(r+\tfrac{1}{2})}{(2r)!\Gamma(n+r+1)}.$$

$$= 2^{n+1} i \sin(n+\tfrac{1}{2})\pi \Gamma(n+\tfrac{1}{2})\Gamma(\tfrac{1}{2}) J_n(z).$$

Hence

$$J_n(z) = \frac{\Gamma(\tfrac{1}{2}-n)(\tfrac{1}{2}z)^n}{2\pi i \Gamma(\tfrac{1}{2})} \int_C (t^2-1)^{n-\frac{1}{2}} \cos zt \, dt$$

so long as $1/\Gamma(\tfrac{1}{2}-n) \neq 0$. This formula, with $C$ having the meaning defined above, proved for $R(n+\tfrac{1}{2}) > 0$, holds for all values of $n$ by analytic continuation.

We have not considered any of the recurrence or other formulae for the special functions involved. The few special results dealt with above have been chosen to illustrate how certain contour integrals, usually concerning many-valued functions, enter into the theory of the above special functions. For further information the reader is referred to larger treatises.†

## Examples 8

**1.** Show that if $\mathscr{R}z > 0$, $\int_\Gamma (-t)^{-z} e^{-t} dt \to 0$ as $r \to \infty$, if $\Gamma$ is either of the quadrants of circles of radius $r+1$ with centres at $-1$, the end points of the quadrants being $r$, $-1+i(r+1)$ and $r$, $-1-i(r+1)$. Deduce that

$$\lim_{r \to \infty} \int_{-1+ir}^{-1-ir} (-t)^{-z} e^{-t} dt = \lim_{r \to \infty} \int_C (-t)^{-z} e^{-t} dt,$$

where $C$ is the contour of Fig. 16.
Hence show that

$$\frac{1}{\Gamma(z)} = \frac{1}{2\pi} \int_{-\infty}^{\infty} e^{1+iu}(1+iu)^{-z} du = \frac{e^{\frac{1}{2}\pi}}{\pi} \int_0^{\frac{1}{2}\pi} \cos(\tan\theta - z\theta) \cos^{z-2}\theta \, d\theta.$$

[Put $t = -1 + i \tan \theta$.]
**2.** Prove that, if $\mathscr{R}(s) > 1$,

$$(2^s-1)\zeta(s) = \zeta(s, \tfrac{1}{2}) = \frac{2^s}{\Gamma(s)} \int_0^{\infty} \frac{x^{s-1} e^x}{e^{2x}-1} dx.$$

† See, e.g., Whittaker and Watson, *Modern Analysis*, et al.

**3.** By taking the contour $C$ in Schläfli's integral (§ 8.6) to be the circle

$$|t-z| = \sqrt{|z^2-1|}$$

show that, if $n$ is an integer,

$$P_n(z) = \frac{1}{2\pi} \int_{-\pi}^{\pi} \{z + \sqrt{(z^2-1)}\cos\phi\}^n \, d\phi. \tag{1}$$

Deduce that if $z$ is real and $z > 1$

$$P_n(z) = \frac{1}{\pi} \int_0^{\pi} \{z + \sqrt{(z^2-1)}\cos\theta\}^{-n-1} \, d\theta.$$

Show also that, if $n$ is unrestricted, (1) holds provided $|\arg z| < \frac{1}{2}\pi$, where

$$\arg\{z + \sqrt{(z^2-1)}\cos\phi\}$$

is taken equal to $\arg z$ when $\phi = \frac{1}{2}\pi$.

**4.** Deduce from § 8.9 that, if $\mathscr{R}(n+\frac{1}{2}) > 0$,

$$J_n(z) = \frac{2(\frac{1}{2}z)^n}{\Gamma(n+\frac{1}{2})\Gamma(\frac{1}{2})} \int_0^{\frac{1}{2}\pi} \sin^{2n}\phi \, \cos(z\cos\phi) \, d\phi,$$

and that, if $\mathscr{R}(n) > 0$,

$$J_n(z) = \frac{(\frac{1}{2}z)^n}{\Gamma(n+\frac{1}{2})\Gamma(\frac{1}{2})} \int_0^{\pi} \cos(z\cos\phi) \sin^{2n}\phi \, d\phi.$$

# BIBLIOGRAPHY

E. T. COPSON, *Functions of a Complex Variable*, Oxford, 1935.
P. DIENES, *The Taylor Series*, Oxford, 1931.
H. and B. S. JEFFREYS, *Mathematical Physics*, Cambridge, 1946.
H. KOBER, *Dictionary of Conformal Representations*, Dover Publ., 1957.
E. LINDELÖF, *Le Calcul des Résidus*, Paris, 1905.
J. E. LITTLEWOOD, *Theory of Functions*, Oxford, 1944.
Z. NEHARI, *Conformal Mapping*, New York, 1952.
G. PÓLYA and G. SZEGÖ, *Aufgaben und Lehrstätze aus der Analysis*, Berlin, 1925.
E. C. TITCHMARSH, *Theory of Functions*, Oxford, 1932.
E. T. WHITTAKER and G. N. WATSON, *Modern Analysis*, Cambridge, 1920.

# INDEX

137

# OTHER TITLES IN THE SERIES IN
# PURE AND APPLIED MATHEMATICS